Connect to NCTM Standards 2000

Making the Standards Work at Grade 8

Francis (Skip) Fennell, Ph.D.

Honi J. Bamberger, Ph.D.

Thomas E. Rowan, Ph.D.

Kay B. Sammons

Anna R. Suarez

Creative Publications®
A Tribune Education Company

Acknowledgments

Project Editors → Diane Nieker, Jeff Stiegel

Writers → Tim Burnett, Marilyn Davis, Beth Sycamore

Writing and Editorial Services → MathLink, Inc.

Design Director → Karen Stack

Design → Gerta Sorensen-London

Project Coordinator → Barbara Quincer

Cover Illustration → Jim Dandy

Illustrators → Susan Aiello, Jim Dandy, Sarah Frederking

Production → Inkwell Publishing Solutions, Inc.

Manufacturing → Dallas Richards

This is an independent publication and is not affiliated with, or sponsored by, the NCTM. The NCTM 2000 Standards are not reproduced in this book. This book is designed to be read independently of the *Principles and Standards for School Mathematics* and to aid educators in preparing to teach in a manner consistent with the *Principles and Standards*.

ISBN 0-7622-1250-0
Catalog No. 21808
Customer Service 800-624-0822
http://www.creativepublications.com
1 2 3 4 5 6 7 8 MAL 05 04 03 02 01 00

Contents

| | Introduction | iv |
| | **About the Standards** | 2 |

	Standard 1: Number and Operation	16
Standards-Based Lessons	Finding Least Common Multiple	18
	Subtracting Integers	24
	Using Inverse Relationships	30
Revised Textbook Lesson	Adding Integers	36

	Standard 2: Algebra	42
Standards-Based Lessons	Graphing Inequalities	44
	Understanding Rate of Change	50
	Exploring Families of Graphs	56
Revised Textbook Lesson	Solving One-Step Multiplication and Division Equations	62

	Standard 3: Geometry	68
Standards-Based Lessons	Identifying Parallel and Perpendicular Lines	70
	Understanding Similarity	76
	Exploring Tessellations	82
Revised Textbook Lesson	Investigating Congruent Figures	88

	Standard 4: Measurement	94
Standards-Based Lessons	Relating Surface Area and Volume	96
	Investigating Rates	102
	Creating Scale Drawings	108
Revised Textbook Lesson	Exploring Angle Relationships	114

	Standard 5: Data Analysis and Probability	120
Standards-Based Lessons	Calculating Probability	122
	Representing Data in Different Ways	128
	Modeling Data with Scatterplots	134
Revised Textbook Lesson	Interpreting and Making Box-and-Whisker Plots	140

| | **Create Your Own Lesson** | |
| | Using Percentages | 146 |

Overview

Since *Curriculum and Evaluation Standards for School Mathematics* was released in 1989, much has been learned about how ideas work in the classroom and how students learn mathematics. The release of the *Principles and Standards for School Mathmatics* creates an opportunity for us to examine our goals, our math curricula, and our teaching methods in light of these new insights and to consider practices and procedures that will improve school mathematics education. As did the original draft, *Principles and Standards* promotes ways for all educators to strengthen the teaching and learning of mathematics by addressing two important concerns: the characteristics of instructional programs that will provide high-quality mathematical experiences for students as they progress through school, and the mathematical content and processes students should know and use as they advance from grade to grade.

General Overview

Connect to NCTM Standards 2000 is designed to help you understand and implement the NCTM standards. Regardless of your teaching style, the information presented in this book will help you to make the standards work. *Principles and Standards* identifies ten standards. Five of those standards are described as content standards that organize all of mathematics into five broad areas of learning; they address *what* students learn. The other five standards, the process standards, are concerned with *how* students learn and how information is presented.

Today, more than ever, there is a need for all students to have a strong base in mathematics. This means that students do not just memorize facts and procedures, but that they have an understanding of mathematics and mathematical thinking. The interplay between content and process is complicated, but integrating the two is critical if our students are to receive the mathematics education they will need to function effectively in the world they will grow into.

The lessons contained within *Connect to NCTM Standards 2000* are organized into sections by content. Each section contains four lessons dealing with some aspect of that content standard. Each lesson demonstrates ways to develop the content by using the process standards. An overview highlights grade-level content skills and gives a brief description of the four lessons for that standard.

Content Standards

Number and Operation

Algebra

Geometry

Measurement

Data Analysis and Probability

Process Standards

Problem Solving

Reasoning and Proof

Communication

Connections

Representation

The last section of the book, entitled Create Your Own, is designed to help you develop lessons of your own that will comfortably incorporate the NCTM standards with your teaching style.

About the Lessons

Each content standard section contains four lessons that address some aspect of the content at the grade level. Three of the lessons have been specially developed to model ways the process standards can be used to develop the content being presented. The fourth lesson examines a typical math textbook lesson in terms of how the process standards are incorporated into that lesson. Suggestions are offered for increasing the focus on three of the five process standards to create a more effective lesson. Then a lesson is presented modeling how those suggestions can be implemented.

As you read through the lessons, keep in mind that what is offered is only one possible approach. You might have a completely different idea about how to develop the concept, and that's fine. These lessons are intended to provide examples of how the process standards can work to make mathematics lessons more meaningful, and, to model questions and techniques that you might incorporate into your teaching. As you read through the lessons, pay attention to how the process standards are being used. Use the ideas presented as a springboard for your own ideas.

Each lesson is intended for a single class period. Some introduce a concept, others require students have some experience with the concept, and still others are meant to be used at the end of a unit. As you examine these lessons, think about how and where they fit into your curriculum. Any of the lessons here can be used as a replacement for the comparable lesson in your current math program. Try the lessons and see the difference incorporating the process standards can make.

Creating Your Own Lessons

The last section of the book is designed to help you develop lessons of your own that incorporate the NCTM standards and are compatible with your teaching style. You will find questions to help you focus on ideas to consider as you begin to organize a standards-based lesson. You will also have an opportunity to follow the thoughts and decisions one person used in the process of developing a lesson.

About the Authors

Francis (Skip) Fennell, Ph.D.

Dr. Fennell was a member of the writing team of *Principles and Standards for School Mathematics* (NCTM, 2000). He has authored mathematics textbooks, materials for both students and teachers, and numerous articles for leading mathematics journals. Dr. Fennell has served on the Board of Directors of NCTM and as Program Officer of instructional materials and teacher enhancement within the Division of Elementary, Secondary, and Informal Education at the National Science Foundation. He has been selected as Outstanding Mathematics Educator by the Maryland Council of Teachers of Mathematics, and as Professor of the Year by both the Carnegie Foundation and Western Maryland College, where he is a professor of education.

Honi J. Bamberger, Ph.D.

Dr. Bamberger is a recognized math scholar and teacher. She has taught at both the elementary school and college levels, served as an associate research scientist and mathematics consultant for Johns Hopkins University, and contributed as a consultant and content writer for the "Numbers Alive" public television series. Dr. Bamberger has presented her research findings at mathematics conferences across the country, and has been an author for a number of mathematics textbooks. Currently, Dr. Bamberger is executive director of Insight, a consulting firm specializing in professional development in mathematics education.

Thomas E. Rowan, Ph.D.

Dr. Rowan was a member of the working group that wrote the K–4 section of the *Curriculum and Evaluation Standards for School Mathematics*. Since the Standards were first published, he has worked with many school systems to help bring about the transition to standards-based classroom mathematics instruction in grades K–8. Dr. Rowan is a frequent presenter at NCTM and author of mathematics texts and numerous articles on teaching and learning mathematics. He currently teaches at the University of Maryland where he focuses on methods of teaching elementary school mathematics.

Kay B. Sammons

Kay Sammons is currently Elementary Mathematics Supervisor for the Howard County Public Schools in Ellicott City, Maryland, where she is responsible for curriculum and staff development for elementary teachers. She is a frequent presenter at state and national mathematics conferences. In addition to serving as a reviewer for NCTM publications, she has written textbooks and teacher resource materials. Ms. Sammons was honored as Elementary Mathematics Teacher of the Year by the Maryland Council Teachers of Mathematics and as Outstanding Educator of the Year by that same organization.

Anna R. Suarez

Anna Suarez is a national consultant and program director for K–8 Mathematics at the National Science Foundation in Arlington, Virginia. Her participation in an NSF-funded research study, Cognitively Guided Instruction (C.G.I.), helped to develop teachers' knowledge of students' mathematical thinking as the basis for making instructional decisions. She has written staff development materials for both the *Investigations* curriculum and Insight.

About the Standards

The *Principles and Standards for School Mathematics* are built around ten curriculum standards. Five of those standards address the mathematical content, or body of mathematical knowledge, that students should learn. These content standards prescribe *what* is to be taught in mathematics. The content standards are Number and Operation, Algebra, Geometry, Measurement, and Data Analysis and Prbability.

The other five standards are process standards. The process standards describe *how* the content is delivered. They address how students will acquire the necessary mathematical content and how that knowledge will be applied. The five process standards are identified as Problem Solving, Reasoning and Proof, Communication, Connections, and Representation.

It should be pointed out that the content standards and process standards are not separate subsets of the whole, but are intricately interrelated. How mathematics is learned is as important as what mathematics is learned. The process standards help to "frame" how the content standards are presented.

It is possible to weave the process standards into the teaching of mathematics through a variety of methods. Students can and should be presented with meaningful problems to solve and situations that require them to reason through information to find solutions. They should be asked to defend their solutions and explain their thinking. In presenting a problem to students, connections might be made to a similar problem to build on previous learning. A representative model might be used to enhance students' understanding of a concept. Continuous communication, written and oral, will provide feedback about students' understanding.

For students to become mathematically powerful, it is essential that they be able to use process skills flexibly. They need to practice applying reasoning to solve problems and proving that their solutions are correct. They need to experiment with a variety of representations and have the ability to use them in solving problems and in illustrating their thinking. They should be able to communicate their mathematical thinking and solutions to the teacher and to other students both orally or in writing. Making connections between problems within mathematics is as essential as is making mathematical connections to disciplines outside of mathematics. The importance of how these processes interrelate and work together cannot be overemphasized.

Content Standards

Number and Operation

Algebra

Geometry

Measurement

Data Analysis and Probability

Process Standards

Problem Solving

Reasoning and Proof

Communication

Connections

Representation

Middle School Problem Solving

PROBLEM SOLVING IS AT THE HEART of mathematics—it is what mathematicians do. Balance is achieved through the interrelationship of conceptual learning, basic skills, and problem solving. Students need to develop concepts with concrete representations to ensure understanding and to build a strong foundation. They need basic skills in order to apply their understandings with efficiency. But most importantly, they need good problems to solve, problems in which they can utilize their conceptual understanding and basic skills.

In its simplest form, problem solving means finding a solution when the answer is not readily apparent. Because problem solving does not always follow a uniform plan, students need to develop persistence to be able to work problems through to the end. Sometimes persistence means changing direction. *Well, we know that way doesn't work. What should we try next? Is there another way we can look at this problem?* Questions that encourage students to look for other options should be an integral part of the discussions that take place in mathematics classes.

Choosing problems that have relevance to students is an important factor in creating enthusiasm for problem solving. Often, the enthusiasm of the teacher translates into a positive disposition toward problem solving for students. If statements like, *Now that's an unusual problem. I wonder how we can find the answer,* are part of a teacher's repertoire, students get the notion that problem solving is pretty interesting stuff and they are encouraged to use their own resources to find a path to the solution.

Acquiring a variety of strategies to access for problem solving is essential to experiencing success. Having flexibility to solve problems in different ways enables students to get "unstuck" if they reach a "dead end." Students should be provided with instruction and practice in using a wide range of strategies that they can then draw upon.

When students are presented with a problem that doesn't exactly fit into the context of what they already know, they need to know how to develop strategies based on their previously learned skills and concepts.

This problem was presented to a class of seventh grade students.

> The recipe for the punch that we are serving at the dance on Friday makes 8 gallons. A punch glass holds $\frac{3}{4}$ cup of punch. Will 8 gallons be enough to serve all 75 of the students expected to attend the dance? If not, how much more punch will be needed? Work with your group and show your work on paper. Be prepared to present your solution to the class.

This is a real-world problem that is relevant to students. The wonderful thing is that like most real mathematics problems encountered outside of the classroom, it's a messy problem.

First, students need some information they're not given. Will some students want more than one serving punch? How many students will decline the punch? How many servings at $\frac{3}{4}$ cup each are there in 8 gallons? Second, students will need to decide how and where they can get the information they need. Third, since there is really no precise answer to a problem like this, students will need to use their estimation and reasoning skills.

Each group might approach this problem a little differently. Some will immediately pick up a calculator and start figuring; others might start with a visual representation. In the process of solving the problem, students might approach the head of the dance committee to see how many tickets have been

sold, or they might canvass their friends as to their preference for punch. They might consult a standards measure table to find equivalent measures for cups, pints, quarts, and gallons.

When the task has been completed, each group should have an opportunity to present and defends its solution. A wide range of approaches and solutions will emerge. These different strategies should be compared noting similarities and differences. Students should also be asked to consider which solutions they think work best for the particular problem and why. This opens the door to a rich discussion that will broaden the learning experience for all.

Problem solving is at the core of any mathematics curriculum; it is integral to all mathematical activity. As such, it should permeate the entire mathematics program. Students who are consistently presented with challenging problems learn to develop and apply new strategies. When they are also given opportunities to communicate their strategies with others and reflect on their thinking, their problem solving abilities are further enhanced.

Middle School Reasoning and Proof

REASONING IS FUNDAMENTAL TO THE STUDY of mathematics— it is a state of mind that causes students to explore, to justify, and to validate. It permeates all content areas and all grade levels. Students are reasoning when they interpret data, when they solve problems, and when they view geometric patterns and shapes. As they are presented with new problems, they use reasoning skills to apply previously acquired information and to test the validity of their solutions. Reasoning is the process by which students make sense of mathematics.

As they develop mathematically, students learn that mathematics is a discipline based on an inherent set of rules. Reasoning begins with intuition. This intuition is used by even the youngest children in their efforts to make sense of mathematics, and it should be encouraged as the basis of reasoning at all grade levels. This informal intuition will become the basis for reasoning through representations that are more formal and for proofs based upon the rules.

What are some ways reasoning and proof can be incorporated into the mathematics class? An excellent way is to ask questions that hold students accountable for their thinking. *How did you get your answer? Tell me how you thought about that. Why does your solution work? Do you think that strategy will always work?*

Piaget believed that for students to develop reasoning, it was imperative to have social interaction. A powerful means of achieving this interaction is through mathematical discussions. Designating time during the class for students to put forth their ideas for examination is critical. Students must learn to explain and defend their thinking. They must also learn to detect unsound reasoning in explanations presented by other students. In any given class there will be a wide range of reasoning abilities and it is helpful for students with less mature reasoning to hear from those with well-developed skills. These mathematical discussions increase a student's repertoire of reasoning skills.

What do these mathematical discussions look like? A teacher typically presents a problem to the class that may be related to concepts being studied. A class of sixth grade students working on figuring percentages was presented with the following problem:

What is 75% of 80?

After allowing a few minutes for students to work independently to figure out the solution, the teacher, Mr. Matthews, invited the students to share their solutions and strategies with another classmate.

"How many of you got the same answer as the person you shared with?" Most hands were raised.

"How many of you used the exact same strategy as that person?" Fewer than half the students responded.

"O.K. Let's look at some of the ways you found to solve this problem."

Min Lee volunteered first. "I got 60. I know that 50% of 80 is 40. 25% is half of 50%. Since 50% was 40, then 25% must be half of that or 20. Then I added 40 and 20. I got 60."

"How many of you used Min Lee's method?" Several students raised their hands.

"Who can tell us another way to look at the problem?"

Jack responded. "I know that 10% of 80 is 8. In order to get 70%, I multiplied 8×7 and got 56. But I still need 5% more. I thought 5% is half of 10%, so 5% must be 4. By adding 56 and 4, I got 60, the same as Min Lee."

Several students indicated they were unclear, so Jack repeated the strategy elaborating on his procedure and stopping after each step to clarify.

Stephanie volunteered another method. "75% is the same as $\frac{3}{4}$. I divided 80 into fourths. Each fourth is 20. Three of them are 60."

"I changed 75% to 0.75 and multiplied. 0.75×80 is 60." offered Jose.

As students present their strategies, there should be opportunities to compare the methods to see how they are alike and how they are different. Students should be asked to consider which strategies they think worked best with the particular problem and why.

Discussions like the one above are rich in reasoning and proof. Whether a student is explaining his answer to the class or listening to the explanation of another to see if it makes sense, reasoning skills are being employed. The time spent on conversations like these, with thoughtful questions posed by the teacher to guide the discussion, is invaluable.

Middle School Communication

Whether between teacher and student, between a pair of students, or among groups of students, the communication skills of reading, writing, and listening and speaking provide the means for sharing ideas and promoting mathematical understanding. As students express their ideas through oral and written language, they have an opportunity to clarify their thinking and reinforce their comprehension of the concepts they are working with. By listening to explanations given by their classmates, students are exposed to ideas they may not have thought of. This provides a greater network of connections among ideas and, in turn, enhances learning.

Ample opportunities to discuss mathematical ideas should be provided. One extremely effective technique that was described in the previous section on Reasoning and Proof involves presenting an interesting problem to the class, allowing time to solve the problem, and then asking students to explain how they solved the problem. Providing a forum for a number of different solutions to be presented and defended by students results in rich dialogue. There is a very high level of mental activity associated with social interaction of this nature. Students who are afforded opportunities to take part in these mathematical conversations on a regular basis learn more effectively how to reason and defend their answers. In the process, they also learn to communicate and to clarify and refine their ideas, which leads to deeper understanding.

Elementary teachers lay the groundwork for students to develop facility in communicating their thinking. Children in the primary grades are usually interested in conversing about mathematics with the teacher as well as with others. If children in grades K–2 have had sufficient opportunities to discuss mathematical ideas, they generally are pretty comfortable continuing that pattern in grades 3–5. But all that changes in the middle school years. This period is characterized socially by wanting to fit in. Students become hesitant to put their thinking in front of others for fear of being ridiculed. Because adolescents are highly social, it becomes essential to have them work in groups. This provides them with a structured forum for their social behavior and a sense of camaraderie.

In middle school, mathematics begins to become more abstract. New concepts still need to be introduced conceptually, but students need to move from concrete representations to symbolic notation more quickly. Effective communication of ideas becomes even more important.

This portion of a 7th grade lesson offers an example of how communication was effectively used to develop an understanding of how surface area can vary for a fixed volume. Each student received 8 unit cubes and the class was led through an oral review of surface area and volume through a series of questions.

> **What is the volume of each cube?**
> **What is the total volume of the cubes?**
> **What is the surface area of each cube?**
> **What is the total surface area of the cubes?**

Students were then directed to arrange the 8 cubes in a 2×4 shape. Questions directed their attention to the concept being developed.

> **What is the volume of the figure you made with your cubes? Explain.**
> **Is the total surface area still 48 square units? Explain.**

As students responded to the questions, there was an opportunity to assess their ability to apply the definitions and figure volume and surface area. Any misunderstandings could be immediately addressed and corrected. Information could be expanded upon.

The lesson went on to have students work in pairs to explore other configurations using the 8 cubes and to find their surface areas and volumes and record their findings. A class discussion was held to compare the results. This led to a discussion about what configuration produced the greatest surface area and the least surface area for the same volume. Students went on to explore how symbolic representation could be used to express those relationships.

This approach allowed students to investigate a problem on a conceptual level with concrete objects and communicate understanding of the concepts involved before moving to symbolic representation. They had an opportunity to work together and communicate their ideas with each other as they investigated solutions. Their findings were then discussed in a larger group and there were opportunities to clarify, affirm, and reinforce understanding.

Putting ideas on paper is another means of helping students organize their thinking. The act of writing something down causes a student to reflect on ideas and refine them before committing that thinking to paper. Often, at the end of a lesson students will be asked to communicate what they learned in the problem or investigation they have just completed. This written reflection can be an important tool for teachers in assessing their students' mathematical understanding. Words, pictures, numbers, and symbols are all important parts of written communication that students have at their disposal, and middle school students are becoming much more adept at using mathematical symbols to communicate their thinking. Many teachers use journal writing as a way for students to relate what they know about mathematics.

Students in grades 6–8 should be provided with regular opportunities to use both oral and written language and to share mathematical ideas with their teachers and peers on a daily basis. This exchange will challenge students to reexamine or refine their thinking and will affirm understanding. This process is essential to internalizing mathematics.

Middle School Connections

MAKING CONNECTIONS IN MATHEMATICS is a three-fold process. First, connections are made when one mathematical idea is used to build another. Second, connections are made among different mathematical ideas. Third, connections are made between mathematics and contexts outside the field of mathematics.

Because mathematics is an integrated discipline, treating it as a whole body of knowledge and focusing on the connections that occur naturally adds dimension to ideas and concepts. How is counting related to addition, addition to subtraction, addition to multiplication, multiplication to area? A cohesive curriculum that is clearly articulated from pre-kindergarten through the twelfth grade, one that connects the mathematical ideas within each grade as well as the mathematics between grade levels, is critical if those connections are to take place.

Making connections to prior mathematical experiences is vital for the understanding of how mathematical ideas build on one another. Teachers need to know what mathematics students learned previously in order to build on that knowledge. In a given unit of study, attention should be paid to ensure that mathematics concepts build upon one another from day to day in a coherent manner. Teachers should also be aware of what their students will be studying in subsequent grades so they can lay the foundations for obvious connections to further studies.

Mathematics permeates other curriculum areas and it is found in the everyday experience outside of school as well. The use of shapes and patterns is prevalent in art and architecture; measurement skills and classification skills are important in science; measurement skills and knowledge of fractions are utilized in cooking and in building models; and measurement skills, data gathering, and statistics are applied in the social sciences.

In middle school, students build on the mathematical foundation laid in elementary school. The concepts of fractions, decimals, and percents were introduced informally in grades K–5, but in grades 6–8, the relationships among these forms take on greater focus. Students become aware of the similarities and differences in these representations and learn which is appropriate for a particular situation. Proportional reasoning and algebraic thinking are also major areas of study. The number work developed in intermediate grades is extended to include work with integers.

Computing with integers is a new topic for middle school students, one that can be connected to the study of number relationships that students encountered in elementary school. The number line, something all students have had experience with, is a helpful tool for modeling addition and subtraction with integers.

There are countless ways to make connections with the mathematics studied in the middle grades. For example, students enjoy taking surveys of their peers' preferences in food, music, movies, and games. This can be connected to collecting, organizing, and displaying this data in a way that makes sense, important skills that help students to better understand and interpret information presented in the world around them. Analyzing the data gathered from these surveys can be connected to interesting statistical problems. The teacher might pose the questions or have students generate their own.

Calculating the cost of having a class party that includes refreshments, prizes for games, and paper products is another relevant problem for students in grades 6–8. Such an activity makes connections to the real world and to students' estimation skills, their understanding of ratios, and their knowledge of operations with fractions and decimals. Working in teams, students can generate a menu and figure out how to adhere to a given budget. This kind of problem also encourages cost comparisons among various brands.

It is important for teachers to be conscious of connections that can be made in mathematics and to weave those connections into daily practice. When students are able to connect mathematical ideas both inside and outside of the classroom, they begin to see mathematics as a cohesive body of knowledge.

Middle School Representation

REPRESENTATIONS PROVIDE VEHICLES FOR EXPRESSING and internalizing mathematical thought. They include physical objects, pictures, and symbols; and they encompass mental images, words, and ideas as well. Representation is a critical component in shaping the way students access, understand, express, and utilize mathematical ideas

Representations can be formal or informal. Examples of formal representations are the conventional symbols, graphs, diagrams, and so on traditionally introduced in school mathematics. More informal forms are often invented by students as a way of making sense of mathematical ideas and communicating those ideas to classmates or the teacher. Connecting to these informal forms will facilitate a meaningful transition to thinking and communicating in the language of mathematics.

As teachers design lessons, choosing the type of representations they feel will best help students understand a concept becomes an important consideration. What shared mathematical language is needed to effectively communicate ideas? What manipulatives or models will be appropriate? How will students record their understanding of the concept? When is it appropriate to move from physical to symbolic representations?

Students at the middle-school level use informal methods to help them interpret ideas that are more complex. For example, before introducing the formula for finding the volume of rectangular solids, a teacher might assign the following task to groups of four:

> Using centimeter cubes, build a variety of rectangular solids. Record the length, width, and height of each one you build. Also, record the number of cubes used to build each figure.

As the students build their solids and record information, the teacher can move among the groups asking questions. The lesson can conclude with a discussion about the relationships between the dimensions of the solids and the number of cubes used to build them. Students share the charts they made which clearly show that the number of centimeters used was equal to the length times the width times the height of the solid.

Rectangular Solids

Length	Width	Height	Total Cubes
2	2	2	8
3	2	2	12
3	3	2	18
3	3	3	27
4	3	2	24
4	4	2	32
4	4	3	48
4	4	4	64

The students are then ready to be presented with the symbolic representation $V = l \times w \times h$, the formula used to find the volume of a rectangular solid.

In this example, using physical representation by building models provides direct experience with the relationships among the length, width, and height and the volume of a figure. This allows students to establish a mental representation of the relationships, so the abstract equation will make sense to them. These students are much more likely to remember the formula.

Conclusion

The process standards are not an end in, and of, themselves. Rather, they provide the advanced organizers, or plan, for lessons that present important mathematics content. Seeing connections among mathematical topics enables students to reason and make sense of new ideas and problem-solving situations they encounter. Through the process of communication, students are able to represent these new ideas either formally or informally.

Just as process standards are interrelated, so are the process and content standards. For true mathematical thinking and learning to occur, both process and content need to be skillfully woven into and through each lesson. That is the goal to work toward.

Standard 1 **Number and Operation**

AT THE EIGHTH GRADE LEVEL, number and operation includes work with integers and the four basic operations, number theory topics, and using inverse relationships to solve problems. Our lessons are derived from these important topics, and include a lesson that focuses on adding integers, a lesson on subtracting integers, a lesson on finding the least common multiple, and a lesson on using the inverse operations multiplication and division to solve problems.

Three lessons model how the process standards can be used to teach content. A fourth lesson is a hypothetical textbook lesson that we have revised to be more standards based. These four lessons do not represent the entire curriculum, but rather provide glimpses of how, with a more concentrated effort to incorporate the process standards, better mathematics teaching and learning can be achieved.

One lesson we have chosen explores the number theory topic of finding the least common multiple. This lesson takes a problem-solving approach in which students develop their own methods for solving problems requiring them to find the least common multiple. Using communication and reasoning and proof, students discuss their methods and make generalizations.

Another lesson we have chosen develops the concept of subtracting integers. The process standards are apparent here as students make connections to subtracting integers in real situations, and relating the subtraction of integers to addition. Students use various representations to model subtracting integers and use reasoning and proof to generate their own set of rules for subtracting integers.

A third lesson that we have chosen focuses on the inverse relationship between multiplication and division. Students use this relationship to solve problems. Students make connections to other inverse relationships and apply their knowledge to solving equations. Students use representation and communication to model how inverses are used and to discuss their solutions and how inverses were used.

The hypothetical textbook lesson that we have chosen to revise is a lesson on adding integers. Rather than a lesson that presents a horizontal number line and a set of rules, this lesson incorporates more representation, communication, and reasoning and proof. From the various representations, students discuss and formulate their own set of rules for adding integers.

Standard 1 Lessons

Finding Least Common Multiple

Subtracting Integers

Using Inverse Relationships

Adding Integers

Finding Least Common Multiple

Introduction

Objective → Students will solve problems that require finding the least common multiple.

Context → This lesson occurs midway in a unit on number theory. Students have learned about primes and factors. They will learn more formal methods for finding the least common multiple.

NCTM Standards Focus

Students are often encouraged to memorize given rules for determining least common multiples in preparation for adding and subtracting fractions with unlike denominators. They may not then understand the concept behind those rules. In this standards-based lesson, students are encouraged to explore common multiples using their own methods. Once they have grappled with different ways of finding multiples and least common multiples, students are better prepared to understand more formal approaches.

Problem Solving Students solve problems that require finding the least common multiple. They come up with their own methods of finding the least common multiple in preparation for learning more formal methods in subsequent lessons.

Communication Students work together to solve the problems presented, then present their solutions to the class. Students are encouraged to use diagrams to help communicate their thoughts.

Reasoning and Proof Students summarize different methods presented into more general statements.

Teaching Plan

Materials → Student pages 22–23

ARRANGE STUDENTS IN PAIRS. Distribute student page 22 to each pair of students. Do not provide any hints on how to solve the problems at the beginning. Just instruct the students to record their methods and solutions. This is an excellent way to incorporate problem solving into a lesson in which it does not always occur. Many times teachers will simply present methods for finding the least common multiple.

As students work on the problems, circulate among the groups. Observe how each group approaches the problems, what knowledge they apply to the problems, and whether they realize that all of the problems are similar.

After an appropriate amount of time (about half the class period), bring the students together and have them share their methods and strategies with the class.

Methods Students Might Use

Problem 1

1. List multiples of 5 and 8 in a chart to show that the two numbers have 40 in common.

5	10	15	20	25	30	35	40	45	50
8	16	24	32	40	48	56			

2. Since the 2 numbers have only a factor of 1 in common, multiply 5 × 8 to get 40.

The shortest length crate the company could use is 40 inches.

Problem 2

1. The first multiple of 18 is 18, but 12 does not divide it evenly. The next multiple of 18 is 36. Since 12 does divide it evenly, 36 is the least common multiple.
2. Make a chart listing the multiples of 12 and 18. Since 36 is the first common multiple, it is also the least common multiple.
3. Since 6 is the greatest common factor of the two numbers, multiply 12 × 18 and divide the result by 6.

Tully and Melinda should use 36 as the lowest common denominator.

Problem 3

1. Make a chart listing the multiples of 15 and 45. Since 45 is the first multiple of 45, and it is the first common multiple, it is the least common multiple.
2. The first multiple of 45 is 45. Since 15 divides 45 evenly, 45 is the least common multiple.

The shortest square the company could build is 45 feet on a side.

Problem 4

1. Make a diagram of multiples of 150. Then begin listing multiples of 250. The least common multiple of the two numbers is 750.

150	300	450	600	750	900	1,050	1,200
250	500	750	1,000	1,250			

2. The first multiple of 250 is 250, but 150 does not divide it evenly. The second multiple of 250 is 500, but 150 does not divide it evenly. The next multiple of 250 is 750. Since 150 does divide it evenly, 750 is the least common multiple.

Erik's and Anne's families must each drive 750 miles before they stop at the same rest stop.

What Might Happen . . . What to Do

Some students might just multiply the two numbers and give the product as an answer to every problem. Have them reread the problems and focus on the words that denote least common multiple, such as "lowest number," "shortest distance," etc. Encourage students to tell in their own words why just multiplying the two numbers might not give them the asked for answer.

Begin your class discussion by asking what the four problems have in common. (All are based on finding the least common multiple.) Ask students to summarize the different methods. Rather than listing them yourself, this gives students an opportunity to use their reasoning. They have to synthesize what they have heard, possibly stated in different terms, and express it in one general statement.

1. Make a chart listing the multiples of each number. The first common multiple is the least common multiple.

2. Find successive multiples of the larger number. The first multiple that the lesser number divides evenly is the least common multiple.

3. Multiply the numbers and divide by the greatest common factor.

4. Multiply the numbers that have only a common factor of 1.

The methods in items 1, 2, and 4 will likely be mentioned, but the method in item 3 may not be. You might want to lead students to it, as it is the more general case for the method listed in item 4, or wait for the more formal presentation of methods for finding the least common multiple in a future lesson.

Have students retry one of the four problems from the in-class activity that they may have had some difficulty solving earlier, using a method that they learned from the discussion. Then have them find the least common multiple of 10 and 14 (70). A good reasoning and communication question to ask is *Are you finding some methods to be more efficient than others in certain situations?* Students are asked to evaluate and discuss the different methods.

Student Pages

Student page 22 contains the problems to be used for the in-class activity. Student page 23 provides more practice problems.

Assessment

You observed students use a problem-solving approach to solve problems dealing with finding the least common multiple. They used their knowledge of multiplication facts and factors in their solution processes. They created lists of multiples and determined that the lowest multiple common to both numbers was the solution to the problem. They also used their knowledge of factors as they multiplied two numbers that had no common factor except 1.

NCTM Standards Summary

Students used the problem-solving standard to develop methods and strategies for finding the least common multiple in each problem. They also used communication as they worked in pairs to explore, discuss, and share their informal methods. They tried out methods that were introduced in class discussion and used their problem-solving skills to determine whether or not all methods worked in all situations. Finally, they used reasoning and proof to generalize about applicable rules and about how to determine the most efficient method in certain situations.

Answers

Page 22
Answers are within lesson.

Page 23
1. 24
2. 66
3. 80
4. 120
5. 60
6. 100
7. 42 inches
8. 200 miles
9. Answers will vary.

Finding Least Common Multiple

Solve the problems.
Write how you solved them.

❶ A company ships its product in two different-sized boxes. One box is 5 inches long and the other is 8 inches long. The company ships only one size box in each crate. What is the shortest length crate the company can use to ship its product in either sized box without having any extra space?

❷ Tully and Melinda are measuring the length and width of a rectangle, but they have different measuring sticks. Tully measured the length to be $9\frac{5}{12}$ inches and Melinda measured the width to be $5\frac{11}{18}$ inches. To add the fractions to find the perimeter, what would they have to use for the lowest common denominator?

❸ A construction company uses 15-foot long concrete blocks for the width and 45-foot long blocks for the length of any rectangular building. What is the shortest length square building the company could construct?

❹ On Sunrise Highway there are rest stops every 50 miles. Erik's family stops at the rest stops every 150 miles. Anne's family stops every 250 miles. The two families began their trips from the same place. What is the shortest distance the two families must drive before they stop at the same rest stop?

Finding Least Common Multiple

**Find the least common multiple
for each pair of numbers.**

1 8 and 12

2 6 and 11

3 10 and 16

4 20 and 24

5 15 and 60

6 4 and 50

Solve the problem.

7 A company ships its product in two different-
sized boxes. One box is 6 inches long and the
other is 14 inches long. The company ships only
one size box in each crate. What is the shortest
length crate the company can use to ship its
product in either sized box without having any
extra space?

8 A cyclist stops for water every 25 miles. Another
cyclist stops every 40 miles. If the two cyclists
started from the same point, after how many
miles will they stop for water at the same place?

9 Write your own problem that involves finding the
least common multiple. Provide the solution.

Subtracting Integers

Introduction

Objective → Students will understand subtraction of positive and negative integers.

Context → Students have added integers. They will go on to apply their knowledge of adding and subtracting integers to all real numbers.

NCTM Standards Focus

Typically, students are given a definition of *integer* and rules that tell how to subtract positive and negative integers. In this standards-based lesson, students analyze and make sense of integer subtraction problems that have answers given. They generate their own rules and apply them to solve problems and to write their own problems.

Reasoning and Proof Students examine integer subtraction problems and determine rules for subtracting integers.

Connections Students make connections between addition and subtraction of integers. They connect the subtraction sign with real-world situations. They also make a connection between the pairs of inverse operations multiplication/division and addition/subtraction.

Representation Students model the subtraction of integers using a number line or other models they choose. They rewrite subtraction problems as addition problems.

Teaching Plan

Materials → Student pages 28–29; number line

DISTRIBUTE STUDENT PAGE 28, and ask students to analyze the first problem. *Do you agree with the answer? Why or why not?* Observe how they apply their previous knowledge of number lines to their reasoning. Note how they deal with the subtraction sign and whether they see that the second number in the subtraction sentence, the subtrahend, is positive.

Using the numbers in the first problem, how else might you get the answer? How could you use addition to get the answer? Observe whether students understand that they can't simply change the operation sign and get the same answer.

Here are some ideas and approaches students might use:

- Remembering that the numbers that are not signed are positive and that these are subtraction problems, students might use the inverse of 8 and change the subtraction to addition: $2 + (^-8)$.

- Some students might consider real-world examples, such as temperatures above and below zero, gaining and losing yards in football, or deposits and withdrawals from an account.

- Students might use a number line. If so, they might determine that the second number, the subtrahend, moves the answer along the number line in the opposite direction from its sign. So when they subtract a positive subtrahend, they start with the minuend and move in the negative direction, and when they subtract a negative subtrahend, they move in the positive direction.

Have students work in groups to analyze the problems on student page 28, using whatever methods make sense to them. Have them tell you what the integers in the different problems represent and how the subtraction sign acts on the integers. When they have finished, have them share their work with the class.

Methods Students Might Use

- Students can use real-life situations to model the problems and help think them through. Gaining and losing yards in football is a likely choice. For example, in problem 1: The team has the ball and gains 6 yards on a play. In the next play, the team loses 8 yards. Students rewrite the original problem, $6 - (^+8) = ^-2$, to show the ball moving in the wrong direction: $6 + (^-8) = ^-2$.

- Another useful real-life scenario is gaining or losing money. For example, in problem 2, students could say someone owed 4 dollars, so she had $^-4$ dollars. She then borrowed 5 more dollars. The 5 dollars borrowed is a positive amount, but now she's deeper in debt: $^-4 + (^-5) = ^-9$.

- Students can also use a number line to analyze the problems. In problem 3, for example, students might move 5 units to the right, from 0. The subtraction sign would indicate a movement to the left. To move to the left $^-2$ units is the same as moving to the right two units. Thus, $5 - (^-2)$ is equivalent to $5 + (^+2)$, which is 7.

- In problem 4, using the number line, students might start at $^-8$ and move 3 steps to the left. They would then realize they took only the negative sign into account and not the subtraction sign; they reached the same solution they would get if they added 2 negative numbers. They remembered that a double negative is the same as a positive, so they changed the $^-3$ to $^+3$ and rewrote the sentence as $^-8 + 3 = ^-5$.

DISCUSS THE PROCESS of changing subtraction to addition. You can make a connection to multiplication and division. A division problem can be rewritten as a multiplication problem by using the reciprocal of the divisor. For example, $8 \div 2 = 8 \times \frac{1}{2}$. To change subtraction to addition, use the inverse of the subtrahend. For example, $5 - (^-5) = 5 + (^+5) = 10$. Contrast this to changing just the operation sign. *What happens if you use these same integers, $^+5$ and $^-5$, and change the subtraction to addition?* Help students see that, just as $3 - 2$ and $3 + 2$ have different answers, so do $5 - (^-5)$ and $5 + (^-5)$.

Discuss the real-world examples the groups used. Then have students work in groups to write their own word problems that involve the subtraction of integers. Have them exchange problems with another group, solve, and get together to share their solutions.

What Might Happen . . . What to Do

Some students might pay attention only to the operation sign and not to the signs of the integers. Suggest that students rewrite the problems, writing each integer with its sign. (Have them place parentheses around the subtrahend to separate its sign from the operation sign.) Have students evaluate the two expressions $6 + 2$ and $6 + (^-2)$. Point out that by missing the negative in front of the 2, they are considering the number as positive 2.

Student Pages

Student page 28 contains integer subtraction problems to be analyzed by the groups. Student page 29 provides practice in subtracting integers.

Assessment

You have observed how students applied their previous knowledge of adding integers to subtracting integers and how they extended their use of number lines. They compared adding positive and negative numbers to subtracting positive and negative numbers, realizing that they cannot get the same answer by adding and subtracting the same numbers. You observed how students applied their knowledge of inverse operations to subtracting negative integers. You also observed students as they analyzed the way the sign of a subtrahend can be interpreted.

NCTM Standards Summary

Students made connections between addition and subtraction as inverse operations. They connected this relationship to the inverse operations multiplication and division. They also related the subtraction of integers to real-world problems they formulated. They used reasoning and proof as they generalized and applied rules that they formulated by writing and solving integer subtraction problems. Students used representation as they modeled the subtraction of integers with a number line or appropriate real-world situations. They also used their knowledge of inverse operations to rewrite subtraction problems as addition problems.

Answers

Page 28

1 – 4. Answers will vary.

Page 29

1. $^-6$
2. $^-5$
3. 12
4. 0
5. $^-2$
6. $^-1$
7. $^-14$
8. 4
9. $^-4$
10. $^-18$
11. $24 - 8 = 16$,
    They were on the 16-yard line.
12. $^-3 - (12) = {}^-15$,
    The temperature was 15 degrees below zero.

Subtracting Integers

Look at the problems below.
How were they solved?
Write about your reasoning.

❶ $6 - 8 = {}^-2$

_____

_____

_____

❷ ${}^-4 - 5 = {}^-9$

_____

_____

_____

❸ $5 - ({}^-2) = 7$

_____

_____

_____

❹ ${}^-8 - ({}^-3) = {}^-5$

_____

_____

_____

Standard 1 Number and Operation

Subtracting Integers

Solve the subtraction problems.

1 $2 - 8 =$ _____

2 $^-4 - 1 =$ _____

3 $3 - (^-9) =$ _____

4 $^-5 - (^-5) =$ _____

5 $4 - 6 =$ _____

6 $^-7 - (^-6) =$ _____

7 $^-6 - 8 =$ _____

8 $1 - (^-3) =$ _____

9 $^-8 - (^-4) =$ _____

10 $^-9 - 9 =$ _____

Solve the problem.
Write an equation using integers.

11 The school football team had the ball on their own 24-yard line. In the next play, they lost 8 yards. Where were they on the field then?

12 On a cold day in a northern state, the temperature was 3 degrees below zero. During the night, the temperature fell 12 degrees. What was the temperature then?

Using Inverse Relationships

Introduction

Objective → Students will understand that multiplication and division are inverse operations and will write equations to solve problems using the inverse operations.

Context → This lesson comes midway through a unit on solving equations. Students have solved one-step addition and subtraction equations and one-step multiplication and division equations. They will move on to solve more complex equations and word problems.

NCTM Standards Focus

In many programs, students are encouraged to memorize rules for using multiplication and its inverse to solve equations. In this standards-based lesson, students first examine word problems to determine the unknown and write an equation that describes the problem situation. They then use their understanding of inverse operations in the process of solving the problem.

Connections Students connect their knowledge of the operations and their functions to determine the inverses for mathematical phrases or equations. They then apply this knowledge to situations in which equations are used to find solutions.

Representation Students display their knowledge of inverse operations either in equations or in the explanations of problems that they solve.

Communication Students relate a mathematical idea to concepts they are already familiar with. They work out problems and communicate their solutions and notions of inverses as they relate to these problems.

Teaching Plan

Materials → Student pages 34–35

BEGIN THE LESSON BY ASKING STUDENTS what it means to undo something. Present situations and have students tell how they would undo them.

How could you undo something written on the board? (Erase it.)

How could you undo a hole dug by your dog? (Fill it in.)

How could you undo giving $10 to a friend? (Take it back.)

Have students come up with a definition of *undo* and then ask if they know what *inverse* means. One meaning of inverse given in the dictionary is *the opposite of,* or *contrary in nature.* Ask students what they think an inverse operation would do. Students should be able to explain that an inverse operation is an operation that undoes the result of another operation.

Present several situations and ask students to explain what would undo each. Be sure to include situations that represent each of the four operations.

Adding 4 to a number	Dividing a number by 3
Subtracting 10 from a number	Multiplying a number by 2.5

Which operations are inverses of each other? How do you know? (Addition and subtraction are inverses as are multiplication and division.)

Present the following expression.

5 times a number + 6, or 5x + 6

Actively engage students in applying inverses by having them explain how to undo the operations involved. Have students record their responses and state their solution in both words and symbolic form. As students offer their solutions, they should be able to explain that they would first subtract 6 and then divide by 5.

Present several additional expressions and have students first write the order of operations, and then describe inverse operations. Emphasize the importance of working in reverse order to undo the operations. Students can work individually or with a partner to complete this activity.

Expression	Order of Operations	Inverses
4x − 2	4 times a number minus 2	add 2, then divide by 4
$\frac{x}{2}$ + 7	a number divided by 2 plus 7	subtract 7, then multiply by 2
6x + 3	6 times a number plus 3	subtract 3, then divide by 6
2(3 + x)	(3 plus a number) times 2	divide by 2, then subtract 3

As students share their solutions, have them explain how they determined what to do. This will reinforce their thinking about the order in which to work and which operation to use to undo what was done in the original expression.

What Might Happen . . . What to Do

Some students may not understand that when determining the inverse to isolate a variable they need to use the inverse operations in the reverse order. Making a connection between this process and a familiar real-life example might help students understand. To undo or find the inverse of putting on your socks and then your shoes, you must use the inverse actions in the reverse order, taking your shoes off first and then removing your socks.

Distribute student page 34 and tell students they are going to see if they can use this idea of inverse operations in some applications problems. Have students work in groups. Instruct groups to record their reasoning and methods so they can share their steps with the class.

Observe students as they work. As you circulate among the groups, ask students to explain how they determined the initial equation to solve each problem and how they determined its inverse. As they solve the problems, ask them how they know their solutions are correct and how they can check their answers.

After students have solved the problems on page 34, bring them together to share and discuss their methods and solutions. Ask them to explain how the knowledge of inverse operations helped them solve the problems. Encourage students to think about generalizations or ideas that might apply to solving problems with unknowns like these.

Methods Students Might Use

Problem 1

You know that $(4 + 2)$ times a number of containers is 78 peaches. This can be expressed as the equation $(4 + 2)x = 78$, or $6x = 78$. The inverse operation to use is division. To find a single x, divide the left side by 6. Whatever is done on one side of the equation must be done on both sides to keep the equation true. Divide 78 by 6 to get 13.

Answer: Thirteen containers are needed. By substituting 13 for x in the original equation, you get $78 = 78$.

Problem 2

You know that $\frac{5}{6}$ of a number $(\frac{5}{6}n)$ represents the total number of students that came to school. Subtract 30 from $\frac{5}{6}n$ since 30 students went on a trip, then add 48, the number of people in the building that are not students. This gives you $\frac{5}{6}n - 30 + 48$. Since there were 258 people in the building, $\frac{5}{6}n - 30 + 48 = 258$, which can be simplified to $\frac{5}{6}n + 18 = 258$. Eighteen has been added to $\frac{5}{6}n$; to undo the addition, use the inverse operation, subtraction, and subtract 18 from each side, resulting in $\frac{5}{6}n = 240$. Next, since n has been multiplied by $\frac{5}{6}$, use division, the inverse of multiplication, and divide both sides by $\frac{5}{6}$, or multiply both sides by the reciprocal of $\frac{5}{6}$. Or, since $\frac{5}{6}n$ is $5n \div 6$, use the inverse of division and multiply by 6 on both sides of the equation, resulting in $5n = 1440$. To find a single n, use the inverse of multiplication, and divide both sides by 5 to get $n = 288$.

Answer: The school has 288 students. By substituting the solution for n in the original equation, you get $240 = 240$.

Problem 3

You know the poster is 26 inches wide, and that after taking 2 inches from the width, you have $\frac{3}{4}$ of the length. The equation that represents this situation is $26 - 2 = \frac{3}{4}L$, or $24 = \frac{3}{4}L$. Since L has been multiplied by $\frac{3}{4}$, use the inverse operation, division, and divide both sides by $\frac{3}{4}$, or multiply by the reciprocal. Or using inverse operations, multiply both sides of the equation by 4, and then divide by 3. Either way, the solution is $L = 32$.

Answer: The poster is 32 inches long. By substituting the solution for L in the original equation, you get $32 = 32$.

Student Pages

Student page 34 contains the problems to be used for the in-class activity. Student page 35 provides problems for individual practice.

Assessment

As students discussed undoing situations and explained how to undo operations you described, you could determine their understanding of inverse operations. As they translated word descriptions into equations and solved for the variable, you assessed students' ability to apply inverse operations.

NCTM Standards Summary

Connections were made between operations as students discussed undoing situations and undoing an operation by using its inverse. Students reasoned through situations to determine how to represent them with equations and then explained their thinking. Both small-group activities and whole-class discussion provided opportunities for students to share their thinking. After setting up the appropriate equations, they determined which inverse operations to apply in order to solve the equations. By substituting their solutions into the original equations, students proved that their solutions were correct.

Answers

Page 34
1. $(4 + 2)x = 78$; $x = 13$.
   Thirteen (13) containers are needed.
2. $\frac{5}{6}x - 30 + 48 = 258$; $x = 288$.
   There are 288 students enrolled in the school.
3. $\frac{3}{4}x + 2 = 26$ in.; $x = 32$ in.
   The poster is 32 inches long.

Page 35
1. $4(x + \$0.85) = \$26.00$;
   $4x + \$3.40 = \$26.00$;
   $4x = \$22.60$; $x = \$5.65$.
   Each person's share was $5.65.
2. $\frac{2}{7}x - 1 = 3$; $x = 14$.
   The aquarium holds 14 gallons.
3. $34x + 102 = 544$; $34x = 442$;
   $x = 13$.
   He bought 13 yards of lumber.
4. $(95 - 15)\frac{x}{60} = 56$; $\frac{4}{3}x = 56$;
   $x = 42$.
   He drove 42 miles an hour.
5. $(1 - \frac{2}{3})\frac{x}{2} = 135$; $\frac{(\frac{1}{3}x)}{2} = 135$;
   $(\frac{1}{6}x) = 135$; $x = 810$
   There were 810 students in school.

Using Inverse Relationships

Write an equation for each problem, then solve.

Write a brief explanation of how you solved each problem.

❶ There are 4 peaches in each container. You add 2 peaches to each container. How many containers are needed to have exactly 78 peaches?

❷ On Thursday, $\frac{5}{6}$ of the school's student population came to school. Thirty of those students went on a field trip. If there were 258 people in school after the students left for their field trip, and 48 of those people were not students, how many students are enrolled at the school?

❸ Toshio is making a poster that is 26 inches wide. If he were to cut 2 inches off the width of the poster, the width would equal $\frac{3}{4}$ of the length. How long is the poster?

Standard 1 Number and Operation

Using Inverse Relationships

Write an equation for each problem, then solve.
Show your methods for solving.

❶ Marc and 3 friends ordered some food at a restaurant. They each paid an equal share of the bill and the tip. Each person's share of the tip was $0.85. The total bill, including tip, was $26.00. What was each person's share of the bill, not including the tip?

❷ Ayesha added 3 gallons of water to her aquarium. This is 1 gallon short of $\frac{2}{7}$ of the number of gallons the aquarium holds. How many gallons of water does the aquarium hold?

❸ Edward spent $544 on lumber and other supplies. The lumber cost $34 a yard. The cost of his other supplies was $102. How many yards of lumber did he buy?

❹ Miguel drove 56 miles to get to his sister's house. He arrived at his destination 1 hour and 35 minutes after he began the trip. During that time, he stopped for 15 minutes to eat. What was his average speed per hour while he was driving?

❺ Two out of three students in school ordered pizza for lunch yesterday. Half of the rest ordered hamburgers. One hundred and thirty-five students ordered hamburgers. How many students were in school yesterday?

Adding Integers

Introduction

Objective → Students will add integers with like and unlike signs.

Context → Prior to this lesson, students have learned about integers, absolute value, and how to compare integers. Following this lesson, they will learn to subtract, multiply, and divide integers.

Adding Integers

· ·

Explore

Joni had $32 after she was paid, but she owed her mom $27. How much did she have after she paid her mom?

Try

If Joni paid $5 toward a $6 debt, what does she owe now? ⁻6 + 5 or 6 + 5 or 6 + ⁻5? You can use a number line to find out.

⁻6 + 5 = ⁻1

If temperature is 5° and it gets 7° colder, what would the temperature be? You can use a number line to find out.

5 + ⁻7 = ⁻2

What is ⁻5 + ⁻6? You can use a number line to find out.

⁻6 + ⁻5 = ⁻11

Adding Integers

- If the integers have the same sign, add the absolute values and use the sign of the addend.

- If the integers do not have the same sign, find the difference of their absolute values and use the sign of the number with the larger absolute value.

NCTM Process Standards Analysis and Focus

The standards analysis examines how the process standards have been incorporated into the above lesson. By increasing the focus on three of the process standards, a more effective and meaningful lesson can be presented. The suggestions offered can help you to think about how this might be accomplished.

Reasoning and Proof Exercises on the text pages call for mental computation, but the reasoning and generalizing required to complete them is minimal.

Suggestion → Build on students' knowledge of working with whole numbers and have them develop their own rules for adding integers. As a product of their reasoning, their rules will be a natural extension of their

•••

Practice

Find each sum.

1. $4 + {}^-3$
2. $7 + {}^-4$
3. ${}^-4 + 6$
4. $4 + {}^-6$

5. $3 + {}^-9$
6. $8 + {}^-5$
7. ${}^-8 + {}^-4$
8. ${}^-3 + {}^-1$

9. $7 + 7$
10. $6 + {}^-7$
11. $15 + {}^-3$
12. $20 + {}^-43$

Find each sum.

13. $3 + {}^-4 + 7$
14. $2 + {}^-7 + {}^-1$
15. ${}^-8 + 3 + 4$
16. ${}^-6 + {}^-2 + {}^-1$

17. ${}^-5 + 9 + {}^-4$
18. ${}^-4 + {}^-2 + 8$
19. $1 + 6 + {}^-4$
20. ${}^-5 + 11 + {}^-8$

21. $5 + {}^-2 + 3$
22. $12 + {}^-6 + {}^-7$
23. ${}^-3 + 8 + 3$
24. $2 + {}^-6 + {}^-2$

Find each sum.

25. $5 + (6 + {}^-1)$
26. ${}^-1 + (7 + 6)$
27. $(2 + {}^-5) + {}^-4$
28. $({}^-1 + 4) + {}^-8$

29. $9 + ({}^-5 + {}^-4)$
30. $({}^-11 + 5) + 4$
31. ${}^-3 + (8 + {}^-11)$
32. ${}^-9 + (5 + 15)$

Problem Solving

33. Sue owed her dad $15. She got paid $23 for washing cars, bought an $11 shirt and gave the rest to her dad toward her debt. How much does she owe now?

34. Jeremy has $22, an I.O.U. to his sister for $12.60, and a bill for $5.00 for a school trip. How much money does Jeremy have left to buy his parents an anniversary gift?

Mental Math

Use mental math to find each sum.

35. ${}^-5 + 8 + {}^-6 + 5 + 7 + {}^-8 + 6 = \square$

36. $23 + 7 + 10 + {}^-20 = \square$

37. the integers from ${}^-3$ to $+6$

38. the integers from ${}^-11$ to $+11$

39. the integers from ${}^-9$ to $+13$

own understanding and will be more meaningful than a formal textbook presentation to be memorized.

Communication While students may discuss their answer choices for a few in-class exercises, opportunities for significant communication are limited.

Suggestion → Give students an opportunity to work together to write clear, concise rules that relate to any situation involving addition of integers. Providing more opportunities for communication will help students clarify the addition process and identify correct methods for solving problems.

Representation A number line is used to model addition of integers.

Suggestion → Present various representations, including number lines, thermometers, and chip models, to help students understand the addition process. Through representation, students will see how positive and negative units "cancel out" and will develop their mental math abilities.

Problem Solving The section labeled problem solving at the end of the lesson consists of two multi-step word problems.

Connections Some connections are made between integers and situations involving money.

The teaching plan that follows shows how the suggestions for increasing the focus on the process standards can be implemented.

Revised Teaching Plan

BEGIN THE LESSON HAVING students make real-life connections by describing situations in which adding two integers might be required. Remind them that in addition they combine numbers to obtain a sum. Possible responses might include yards gained or lost during a football game, deposits and withdrawals of money, gain or loss in stock prices, travel in opposite directions, rise and fall of temperature, and climbing or descending in an airplane. Have students explain how the integers relate to the situations they describe, and list their responses on the board.

Use the football (or travel) scenario to present the different combinations of integers to be added. *On the first play, the Tigers had a gain of 5 yards. On the second play, they had a loss of 7 yards. How many yards did the team gain or lose in all?* (Loss of 2 yd) *How would we record that addition?* ($^+5 + {^-}7$) Draw a number line, and show students how to use it to find the sum. Emphasize that zero is always the starting point. Ask students in which direction they move to show a positive integer (right); a negative integer (left). Have them state the number sentence that gives the total yardage ($^+5 + {^-}7 = {^-}2$) and interpret the meaning of $^-2$ in the context of the problem. (The team had a loss of 2 yards.) Connecting the visual model of the number line with the symbolic representation gives students another way to understand what happens when integers are added.

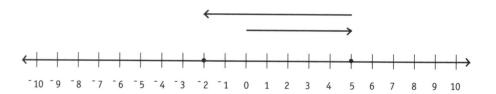

WORK THROUGH SEVERAL MORE EXAMPLES with students, making sure that different combinations of signs are covered. Avoid discussing rules at this point, and focus on familiarizing students with how to use a number line to add integers.

Other Modeling Approaches

Modeling integer addition can be accomplished using chips (or drawings chips) of different colors to represent positive and negative integers. For example, using red for negative and blue for positive integers, students can show adding ⁻5 and ⁺3 with 5 red chips and 3 blue chips, pairing each red with a blue.
The two unpaired red chips represent a sum of ⁻2.

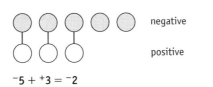

negative

positive

⁻5 + ⁺3 = ⁻2

This method offers a nice visual that clearly illustrates how the number with the greater absolute value gives its sign to the answer. You might have volunteers model several problems using one of these methods.

WRITE SEVERAL ADDITION SENTENCES (with their sums) on the board. Include addition of two positives, two negatives, and positive/negative (including opposites). *Can you think of a way you can predict the sign of the answer?* Students may say something such as "the sum of a positive integer and a negative integer has the sign of the integer that is farther from zero." Ask students how this could be restated using absolute value. This discussion will prepare students for the group activity that follows.

Have students work in groups of three or four. Ask them to write some rules or generalizations about adding two integers. Write the following list on the board to help students organize their thoughts:

- Adding two positives
- Adding two negatives
- Adding zero
- Adding a positive and a negative when
  –positive has greater absolute value
  –negative has greater absolute value
  –integers are opposites

Emphasize that rules should be clear and concise. Suggest that students use number lines to check their rules. Communicating among themselves and using reasoning to generate rules that come from their own understanding of adding integers will be far more meaningful to students than memorizing rules from a textbook.

HAVE GROUPS PRESENT THEIR RULES to the class. Encourage students to comment on the validity and usefulness of each group's rules and compare them to their own. This group interaction will help the individual student to think critically about the addition process and reinforce his or her understanding of how to add integers.

After all groups have made their presentations, work with students to summarize the procedures the class has presented and write a class set of rules for adding integers. To clarify their thinking, ask students questions such as *Without adding, how would you decide if 16 + ⁻29 is positive or negative?*

Close the lesson by having students apply their new rules to find the following sums.

$$^-3 + 7 \qquad 6 + ^-5 \qquad 2 + ^-8 \qquad ^-4 + ^-9 \qquad 7 + ^-12$$

(Answers: 4, 1, ⁻6, ⁻13, ⁻5)

Student Pages

Students are ready to complete practice exercises similar to those shown on the reduced student pages.

Assessment

There were opportunities to determine whether students understood the use of integers as they presented real-life situations with integers and wrote addition sentences. Their understanding of the addition process could be assessed by considering the rules they produced and how well they applied those rules.

NCTM Standards Summary

Students gained insight into the meaning of integer addition by connecting real-life situations such as gains and losses in football with number line representations. Through a rule-writing activity that required a great deal of reasoning and communication, students generated a meaningful set of procedures that resulted from their own understanding of the addition process. Number line and chip model representations helped students visualize the steps involved when they add two integers and provided them with a tool for checking their work.

Standard 2 **Algebra**

AT THE EIGHTH GRADE LEVEL, algebra includes a lot of work with solving equations and inequalities, graphing, and rates and ratios. Our lessons are derived from these important topics, and include a lesson on graphing inequalities, a lesson on rate of change, a lesson that explores families of graphs, and a lesson on solving one-step equations using multiplication or division.

Three lessons model how the process standards can be used to teach content. A fourth lesson is a hypothetical textbook lesson that we have revised to be more standards based. These four lessons do not represent the entire curriculum, but rather provide glimpses of how, with a more concentrated effort to incorporate the process standards, better mathematics teaching and learning can be achieved.

One lesson we have chosen focuses on graphing inequalities on a coordinate plane. Through the process standards of representation, communication, and reasoning and proof, students extend their knowledge of graphing linear functions to graphing inequalities. They develop their own reasoning for determining which half-plane represents the solutions.

Another lesson we have chosen is one in which students relate the slope of a graph to the rate of change of the function. The process standards of representation, reasoning and proof, and communication drive this lesson that has students conclude that slope indicates a rate of change. They see the effect that changing the rates has on slope. Students also use their mathematical vocabulary to explain the "story" represented by a given graph.

A third lesson that we have chosen explores families of graphs. Students use reasoning and proof, representation, and communication to focus on how the slope and y-intercept affect the graph of a line. By keeping one constant, students can see how changing the other makes the graphs different. Students will try to predict the results of a change in either m or b, and will check their predictions by graphing.

The hypothetical textbook lesson that we have chosen to revise is one on solving one-step multiplication and division equations that have fractions or decimals in them. Through better incorporation of the process standards of communication, connections, and reasoning and proof, students not only solve, but discuss and justify their methods of solution. Students see how solving these equations remains consistent with what they have learned about solving other equations.

Standard 2 Lessons

Graphing Inequalities

Understanding Rates of Change

Exploring Families of Graphs

Solving One-Step Multiplication and Division Equations

Graphing Inequalities

Introduction

Objective → Students will graph inequalities on the coordinate plane; given an inequality, students will interpret its meaning.

Context → Students have had experiences graphing simple inequalities on the number line. They have graphed linear functions and are familiar with the idea of slope. Students will go on to solve systems of equations and inequalities.

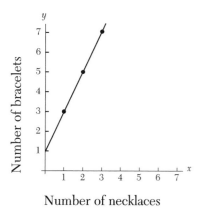

Number of necklaces

NCTM Standards Focus

The visual representation of inequalities will help students understand the nature of a solution set and how to interpret solutions. Sharing ideas will reinforce students' understanding of the steps used for graphing inequalities and will clarify the meaning of sets of points shown on a graph. The lesson is designed to encourage students to reason as they generate their own methods for graphing inequalities on the coordinate plane.

Representation Students use two variables to represent situations involving inequalities, then graph these inequalities on the coordinate plane.

Communication Through discussion and group problem solving, students build on their understanding of graphing linear functions and extend this understanding to graphing inequalities.

Reasoning and Proof Students use reasoning to develop a method for determining which part of the graph of an inequality to shade.

Teaching Plan

Materials → Student pages 48–49; graph paper; straightedge

BEGIN THE LESSON BY PRESENTING the following situation. *The number of bracelets Nia makes in a week is one more than twice the number of necklaces she makes during the same week. What are three possibilities for the number of bracelets and the number of necklaces Nia makes?*

How can you represent this situation algebraically? What does each variable represent? (Let x represent the number of necklaces and y represent the number of bracelets; then $y = 2x + 1$.) *How can you show the solutions to the equation* $y = 2x + 1$? (Draw a graph.) Have students draw the graph. Ask them to describe what each ordered pair represents (a solution) and what each number in the ordered pair represents (x represents a number of necklaces and y represents a number of bracelets). Check students' graphs to be sure they match the graph shown in the margin.

What Might Happen . . . What to Do

Some students might have graphed negative values for *x* and *y*. Point out that for this situation, only non-negative values should be considered, as Nia could not make a negative number of necklaces or bracelets.

Now change the problem slightly:

Nia has found that her business is profitable only when the number of bracelets produced weekly is greater than twice the number of necklaces plus one. What are three possibilities for the number of bracelets and the number of necklaces Nia might make?

How is this problem similar to the previous problem? How is it different? (The number of bracelets cannot be exactly $2x + 1$; it must be more.) *What algebraic representation would you use to represent the new situation?* ($y > 2x + 1$) *If necessary, review the inequality symbols and their meaning with students.*

Ask students to identify a few ordered pairs that satisfy the inequality. Then ask students to think about how the graph they drew for the first problem could help them graph the inequality. Explain that a line separates the coordinate plane into three sections:

- the line itself, where points on the line represent ordered pairs such that $y = 2x + 1$;
- a section where points represent ordered pairs such that $y < 2x + 1$;
- a section where points represent ordered pairs such that $y > 2x + 1$.

In the first problem, points on the line are ordered pairs such that $y = 2x + 1$. Have students try to determine the relationships between the other two sets of points: ($y < 2x + 1$ and $y > 2x + 1$) *Where are these sets of points located?* (on either side of the line) *How can you decide which set of points, or region, corresponds to each inequality?* (Pick two points, one above and one below the line. Substitute to determine the point that satisfies the inequality). *On which side of the line did you find the points that satisfy the inequality for the problem* $y > 2x + 1$? (above the line) *Is the line itself part of the solution set?* (No) Explain that the line is often called the *boundary* for the regions.

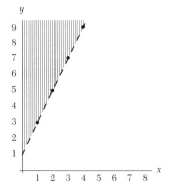

Since the line is *not* part of the solution, it is drawn with dashed lines. The side of the graph containing a point that satisfies the inequality is shaded to show the solution. *How many solutions are there to the inequality?* (Infinitely many) Students should note that only points in the first quadrant are appropriate here, since the number of bracelets or necklaces cannot be negative.

CONTINUE THE DISCUSSION BY asking students what they think the graph of $y \leq 2x + 1$ or $y \geq 2x + 1$ might look like. *How can you show that y can be greater or equal to 2x + 1?* (Use a solid line instead of a dashed line.)

Ask students to summarize the rules for using solid or dashed lines (dashed for an inequality that contains $>$ or $<$; solid if inequality contains $\geq$ or $\leq$). Be sure students understand the reasons for choosing dashed or solid lines, rather than just memorizing the rules. If they understand the rules, students will be able to reason and recreate them later. Ask students to formulate a set of steps for graphing an inequality. Steps should include:

- graph the line (boundary);
- determine if the line should be solid or dashed;
- test a point on either side of the line;
- shade the side whose ordered pair results in a true inequality.

Distribute student page 48. For each problem, students should explain the meaning of the inequality, describe how they determined whether to use a solid or a dashed line and which side to shade, and interpret the solution in the context of the problem.

Problem 1

This week Nia can spend up to $60.00 on supplies. Glass beads cost $2.00 a box and silver beads cost $4.00 a box. Use a graph to find three combinations of beads that Nina can purchase.

Problem 2

One number is greater than four times another number. Graph the possible pairs of numbers.

This problem will allow students to recognize that negative values and non-integral values can be solutions in appropriate situations.

Problem 3

One number is less than 1 less than twice another number. This same number must also be greater than 1 less than one half of the other number. What are three possibilities for the two numbers?

Students should write and graph the two inequalities $y < 2x - 1$ and $y > \frac{1}{2}x - 1$. The numbers that satisfy both inequalities can be found where the shaded regions overlap. Some possible ordered pairs are (4,3), (2,2), and (5,6).

Student Pages

Student page 48 contains the three problems that students work on as part of the lesson. Student page 49 asks students to graph inequalities.

Assessment

You were able to assess students' understanding of algebraic representation and coordinate graphing throughout the lesson. As students used inequalities to solve problems, it was possible to evaluate their understanding of the steps involved in graphing and their ability to interpret the solutions.

NCTM Standards Summary

Representation was a key element of this lesson, as students translated real-world situations into algebraic sentences and then into graphs. This approach also helped students to recognize how algebraic and geometric methods complement each other. Communication enhanced students' understanding of inequalities and supported the reasoning process that resulted in self-formulated guidelines for graphing linear inequalities.

Answers

Page 48
1. Answers will vary.
2. Graph should show dashed line at $y = 4x$, shaded region above the line
3. Answers will vary.

Page 49
1–8. Check students' graphs.
9. $y \leq 15x$
10. $y > 2x$

Graphing Inequalities

❶ This week Nia can spend up to $60.00 on supplies. Glass beads cost $2.00 a box and silver beads cost $4.00 a box. Use a graph to find three combinations of beads that Nia can purchase.

❷ One number is greater than four times another number. Graph the possible pairs of numbers.

❸ One number is less than 1 less than twice another number. This same number must also be greater than 1 less than one half of the other number. What are three possibilities for the two numbers?

© Creative Publications. Permission is given by the publisher to reproduce this page for classroom use only.

Standard 2 Algebra

Graphing Inequalities

Graph the inequality.

1 $y > ^-x + 2$

2 $y > \frac{1}{2}x$

3 $y < 2x$

4 $y > 3x - 1$

5 $y \leq 2x + 1$

6 $y < \frac{1}{3}x + 1$

7 $y > x - 3$

8 $y \geq \frac{-1}{2}x + 2$

Write and graph an inequality to represent each problem situation.

9 Ina is planning a party for her parents. She has decided to spend no more than $15.00 per person. How much might Ina spend?

10 Mike always scores more than twice the number of baskets that Jamal scores. What are possible sets of scores for Mike and Jamal?

Understanding Rates of Change

Introduction

Objective → Students will develop an understanding of the rate of change of a function and the slope of the graph of the function.

Context → Students will build on their ability to graph linear equations using ordered pairs. They will advance to graphing an equation using the slope-intercept form.

NCTM Standards Focus

By developing visual representations of real-world situations, students will learn to recognize the relationship between the slope of the graph and the rate of change of the function. By drawing inferences from the appearance of different graphs, they will develop insight into the relationship between slope and the behavior of a linear function. As students make their own graphs, they will become proficient at formulating explanations of the graphs.

Representation Students translate real-world situations into algebraic symbolism and represent the relationships graphically.

Reasoning and Proof Students experiment with changing rates and make generalizations about the effect of changing rates on slope.

Communication As students explain the "story" shown in each graph, they have opportunities to organize ideas and use mathematical vocabulary.

Teaching Plan

Materials → Student pages 54–55; graph paper; straightedge

BEGIN THE LESSON with a quick review of the distance formula, $d = rt$ (distance = rate × time). Distribute graph paper. Explain to students that they will draw a graph of a family's automobile trip. Have them set up axes showing one-hour intervals on the horizontal axis and 10-mile intervals on the vertical axis. Present the following situation.

The family left home at 9 a.m. At 10 a.m., the odometer showed the family had traveled 50 miles. Ask students what the average rate of speed was for this part of the trip. *How did you decide? What is the equation for the rate of speed for this portion of the trip?* ($50 = 1r$; $r = 50$ mph, $d = 50t$) Have students graph this part of the trip.

Present the next portion of the family trip scenario. *Traffic increased as it got later. By noon, the family had traveled a total of 110 miles. What was their average speed for this part of the trip?* Have students explain how they determined the new average speed. [$d = 110 - 50$ (the number of miles traveled from 10:00 until noon); $t = 3 - 1$ (the number of hours from 10:00 until noon) $60 = 2r$; $r = 30$ mph; $d = 30t$] Have students graph this segment of the trip.

At this point, the family stopped for lunch. They ate lunch from noon until 1 p.m. What was the distance traveled? (0 miles) *What was their average speed?* (0 mph) Have students graph this portion of the trip.

Because of heavy highway traffic, the family had traveled only a total of 140 miles by 3 p.m. Repeat the questioning used above to have students determine the average rate of travel for this leg of the trip. Have students graph their results and then discuss the graphs. *How does the average speed relate to different portions of the graph?* (The greater the rate, the greater the inclination or slope of the graph.) *Which portion of the graph has a slope of 0?* (The portion that represents when the family had lunch.) Explain that the ratio that gives the average rate of speed in each situation is the slope of the corresponding part of the line graph:

$$\text{Average speed} = \text{slope} = \frac{\text{change of distance}}{\text{change in time}} = \frac{d2 - d1}{t2 - t1}$$

Family Auto Trip

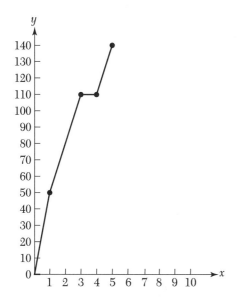

f.y.i.

If students have not worked with slope recently, you may want to briefly review the definition of slope and the method for finding the slope of a particular line.

Note that as the rate decreases, the line still rises from left to right as time continues, but the rise is not as steep. Engage the students in a *what if* discussion. *What if, at 3 p.m., the family boarded an airplane and traveled an additional 1200 miles by 6 p.m.? How would this portion of the graph look?* (steep) *Why? What if the family could take a rocket and travel 100 miles in just 1 second? What would the graph look like for this part of the trip?* (Very steep, almost vertical because the rate of change is so great and because of the size of the intervals shown on this graph.)

REINFORCE THE RELATIONSHIP between slope and equations that describe a constant rate of change. Provide students with the following example. *Suppose Alan bicycles at the rate of 5 mph, while Brenda cycles at 8 mph.* Have students represent the time/distance relationship for both cyclists on the same graph. Ask them to explain why the line showing data for Brenda lies above the line showing data for Alan. (Brenda's rate is greater, so her line has a steeper slope. She covers more distance in the same amount of time.) Ask students to add a line for Carlo, whose rate is greater than Alan's, but less than Brenda's. *How did you decide where to put the line? How does the slope of Carlo's line compare to Brenda's and Alan's?* (It is greater than Alan's, but less than Brenda's.) *What is the equation of Alan's line?* ($d = 5t$) *What is the slope of Brenda's?* ($\frac{8}{1}$)

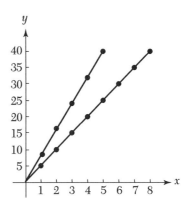

You may wish to illustrate situations involving rates other than speed, for example, earnings per hour or miles per gallon. Ask questions to emphasize the relationships among slopes of lines representing similar rates. *If Kathy earns twice as much per hour as Lucas, how do the slopes of lines showing their earnings compare?* (The slope of the line showing Kathy's earnings is twice as great or steep as the slope of the line showing Lucas' earnings.)

Have students explore a negative rate of change. *On each of the first 15 days of May, Greg deposits $20. Then for the next five days, he withdraws $20 per day.* Have students draw the graph of days/savings total for the entire 20-day period. Ask them to compare the slopes for each part of the graph and describe what they see happening. They may notice that the slopes are similar, but that they go in opposite directions. *If the slope of the portion showing deposits is $\frac{20}{1}$, what do you think the slope showing the withdrawal period would be?* ($\frac{-20}{1}$) *If the slope of a line is rising, what generalization can* *you make about the slope?* (It is positive.) *If the slope of a line is declining, what generalization can you make about the slope?* (It is negative.)

Conclude the lesson with another activity for students to complete in pairs: Have students write a story and create a graph about a trip involving different rates of speed. Stories can be unrealistic to show the full effect of changes in slope. Pairs should exchange stories and draw graphs of the stories they have received. Allow students to compare their graphs with the graph prepared at the beginning of the lesson. Students should resolve any differences through discussion and cooperative effort.

Student Page

Student page 54 first has students match parts of a graph to a description of what may be occurring in order to create the given line. Student page 55 asks students to describe a situation that a graph might represent. It also provides situations for students to graph.

Assessment

During the lesson you were able to assess students' understanding as they interpreted and graphed the ongoing scenario you presented. Class discussion and individual work on the student pages provided additional assessment opportunities.

NCTM Standards Summary

Students represented real-world situations on graphs and were able to interpret slope as a rate of change. They made comparisons among slopes of different lines and related those to various rates of change. Students used their prior knowledge of the graphing of equations to discover how slope is reflected in each equation. Discussions of travel and other stories provided a context for the exploration of slope and helped students develop insight into the concept. Visual representations also allowed students to generalize the relationships characterized by positive and negative slopes.

Answers

Page 54
1. a, 1; b, 2; c, 4; d, 3
2. a, 4; b, 2; c, 3; d, 1

Page 55
1–2. Check students' graphs.
3.

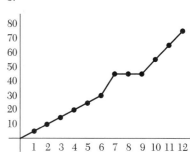

4.

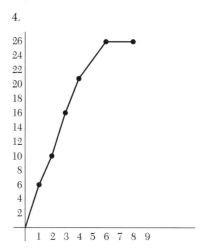

Understanding Rates of Change

Match the parts of the graph identified by the numbers with the descriptions listed.

1

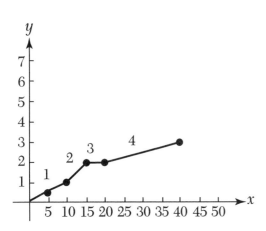

a. Joe jogged.

b. Joe sprinted.

c. Joe walked.

d. Joe stopped for a glass of water.

2

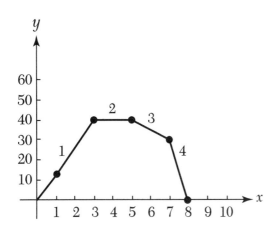

a. Tamika used all her savings to buy gifts.

b. Tamika got sick and did not babysit for two days.

c. Tamika withdrew lunch money for the week.

d. Tamika deposited her babysitting money for three days.

Standard 2 Algebra

Understanding Rates of Change

Write a short story describing what situation each graph might represent.
Label the axes to match your story. Give the graph a title.

❶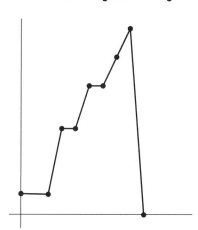

❷

Draw a graph to represent each of the following stories. Label the axes. Give the graph a title.

❸ Ariel received five dollars each day for seven days for feeding her neighbor's pet. At the end of the week, the neighbor gave her a $10 bonus. For two days she didn't make any money. Then another neighbor hired her to watch two cats and a dog for $10 a day for three days.

❹ Ping decided to run a marathon with his father. He ran the first six miles in one hour. Two hours into the race, Ping crossed the 10-mile marker. After that he picked up the pace and again ran six miles in one hour. When he had run a total of four hours, Ping crossed the 21-mile marker. Ping finished the 26 miles after running two more hours. He relaxed at the finish line for two hours while congratulating all of the other runners.

Exploring Families of Graphs

Introduction

Objective → Students will predict how changing the parameters m and b in the equation of a line changes the appearance of the graph.

Context → This lesson comes early in a unit on graphing and functions. Students are familiar with the concept of a function and have graphed linear equations using tables of ordered pairs. They have also learned how to determine slope. Students will go on to write equations of lines and graph linear inequalities and systems.

NCTM Standards Focus

Rather than merely graphing an equation of a line, this lesson challenges students to explore how various representations of a linear equation impact on a graph of the line. Students examine families of related equations, graph lines to represent each member, and then discuss common characteristics. They create additional equations for the family, predict how the new equations will relate to those they have already graphed, and then check their thinking by graphing the equations. Finally, they create and graph equations to fit specific descriptions. Connecting algebra and geometry in this way results in a more meaningful study of slope and intercept.

Representation Students will represent linear equations graphically and relate visual characteristics of the graph to algebraic parameters of the equation. Understanding these correspondences will help students become more proficient at graphing and writing equations.

Reasoning and Proof By exploring families of graphs, students will form conclusions about which parameter affects slope and which parameter affects the y-intercept. Students will make predications about linear functions that have particular "family" characteristics and check their predictions by graphing. This activity will give students experience in making mathematical generalizations and reinforce their understanding of linear functions.

Communication Students will explain their observations about sets of graphs and corresponding equations and evaluate one another's strategies for finding lines with particular characteristics. These discussions will help students extend their analytical thinking skills and provide opportunities to cover a broad range of linear relationships.

Teaching Plan

Materials → Student pages 60–61; graph paper or graphing calculators

INTRODUCE THE LESSON by discussing how, although family members do not look exactly alike, they share some features that help others to recognize them as members of the same family. Ask students to suggest some of these identifying features. Responses might include hair color, shape of the nose or mouth, eye color, height, etc.

Explain that similarly, a family of graphs is a group of graphs that displays one or more similar characteristics. We can think of the most basic, or simplest, graph as the "parent" of the family. In order to recognize the common features of graph families, we graph the groups of equations on the same set of coordinate axes (or on the same screen if graphing calculators are available).

Briefly review the method for graphing linear equations. Model making a table of values with convenient values for x (the independent variable) and finding the corresponding values for y (the dependent variable). Graph the points for the ordered pairs and connect the points with a line to represent the graph of the equation.

Pair students to graph $y = x$; $y = 2x$; and $y = 3x$; and $y = 5x$ on the same set of axes. Have them identify the parent graph $(y = x)$ and describe this family of graphs. Students should observe the following characteristics:

- Each graph is a line through the origin.
- Each line rises from left to right.
- The lines become steeper as the coefficient of x increases.

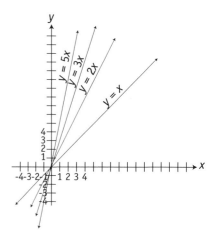

Ask students to write another linear equation with the same characteristics as this family of graphs and predict where the graph of their line will lie in relation to the lines already graphed. Have students explain the reasoning they used in making their prediction to focus thinking on the relationships between the appearance of the line and the coefficient of x.

Have students compare their equations. Ask them to generalize about the relationship between the steepness of the resulting lines and the coefficient of x. Next, suggest they use an equation such as $y = \frac{1}{2}x$ to graph on the same axes and describe the graph of this equation in relation to the others. Then, ask them to find the slope of each line by determining the ratio of the vertical change to the horizontal change and explain their findings. Students should be able to explain that the slope of each line is equal to the coefficient of x in equations of the form $y = mx$.

CONTINUE THE EXPLORATION with a second family of graphs. Ask students to graph $y = {}^-x$; $y = {}^-2x$; $y = {}^-3x$; $y = {}^-5x$; $y = {}^-\frac{1}{2}x$. Have students identify the parent graph $(y = {}^-x)$ and describe the family characteristics. Students should be able to explain the following:

- Each graph is a line through the origin that falls from left to right.

- The steepness of the line increases as the absolute value of *m* increases.

Ask students to write the equation of another graph in the family, predict where it will lie, and check their prediction by graphing. Again, have students determine the slopes and explain the correspondence.

PRESENT A THIRD FAMILY. Ask students to graph $y = 2x$; $y = 2x + 1$; $y = 2x + 3$; $y = 2x - 2$; and $y = 2x - 4$. *What is the parent graph?* ($y = 2x$) *Describe the appearance of this family.* (Parallel lines that intersect the y-axis at different points) *What is the same about each equation?* (The coefficient of *x* is 2 in each case.) *What does this mean?* (The slope of each line is 2.) Have students verify this conclusion by finding the slope of each line. Doing this will reinforce the results that were found earlier in the lesson.

What is different about each equation? (The value of its constant) *With respect to the parent graph, how is this difference reflected in the graphs of the other lines?* Point out that the parent equation can be thought of as $y = 2x + 0$. If the constant is greater than 0, the graph lies above the parent; if the constant is less than 0, the graph lies below the parent. *What relationship do you notice between the value of the constant in each equation and its graph?* (The constant represents the point where the line crosses the y-axis.) Explain that this point is called the y-intercept. For linear equations of the form $y = mx + b$, the constant *b* represents the y-intercept of the graph.

Have students write an equation of another member of this third family, predict where the graph will lie, and then check by graphing. Review their results to be sure they recognize that lines with the same slope are parallel. *Predict the characteristics for the family of graphs that includes* $y = 3x$; $y = 3x + 5$; $y = 3x + 10$; $y = 3x - 6$; $y = 3x - 20$. *What is the equation of another member of this family?*

Write $y = 2x + 3$; $y = 3x + 3$; $y = {}^{-}x + 3$; and $y = {}^{-}4x + 3$ on the board. *What would this group of graphs look like?* (The graphs would be lines with different slopes all passing through the point (0,3).) *Of the lines for* $y = {}^{-}2x + 6$; $y = {}^{-}3x + 1$; *and* $y = {}^{-}2x - 3$, *which are parallel? How do you know?* ($y = {}^{-}2x + 6$ and $y = {}^{-}2x + 3$ are parallel; since the coefficient of *x* is the same, the slopes are the same and the lines are parallel.)

Answers

Page 60

1. Graph B; the form is $y = mx + b$; the coefficient of *x* in each equation is the same; the slope is the same and the lines are parallel.

2. Graph C; each equation has a constant of +4. As a result, each line will pass through 4 on the y-axis.

3. Graph A; these equations are of the form $y = x$, where there is no constant added, so when $x = 0$, $y = 0$. This results in a line that passes through the origin.

4. slope = ${}^{-}2$; y-intercept at 3

5. slope = $\frac{2}{3}$; y-intercept at ${}^{-}2$

6. slope = 1; y-intercept at 2

CONCLUDE THE LESSON by having students write equations and draw graphs for a family with a given set of characteristics, for example, equations for a family of parallel lines with y-intercepts of 3, 7, 0, $^-4$, and $^-8$. Then have students make up their own family description, trade with another group, write the required equations, and graph.

What Might Happen . . . What to Do

- -

Students might misinterpret the graphical relationship with respect to y-intercepts of a family. One line is above or below another line depending on whether its y-inter-

cept is relatively greater or less, and not simply whether it is positive or negative. For example, $y = 2x - 6$ is above $y = 2x - 11$ because $^-6 > ^-11$.

Student Pages

Student page 60 offers students practice in identifying common characteristics of graphs, graphing given equations, and finding slopes and y-intercepts. Student page 61 asks students to write equations and graph lines with given characteristics.

Assessment

Class discussions and graphing activities allowed you to assess how well students understood relationships among equations and their graphs. As students worked on the activities and student pages, you could evaluate their proficiency with graphing techniques and slope calculations.

NCTM Standards Summary

By exploring the common features of algebraic and graphical representations of lines, students identified what the algebraic parameters m and b correspond to in visual terms, making the results about slopes and intercepts more meaningful for students. By examining families of graphs, students had the opportunity to reason and generalize about linear relationships and to explore and look for patterns. Communication was important as students discussed their observations and ideas, ensuring that a broad range of possibilities was included in the lesson.

Page 61
1. All pass through the origin.
2. All have the same slope.
3. All pass through the origin.
4. All have a y-intercept of 5.
5. Possible solutions: $y = 2x + 4$; $y = 2x - 0.5$
6. $y = ^-x$
7. $y = \frac{1}{2}x + 8$
8. $y = 5x - 4$
9. $y = ^-3x + 7$
10. Possible solution: $y = 2x + 2$
11. Possible solutions:
    $y = ^-x$; $y = 0$ $y = ^-3x$; $y = 3x$; all pass through the origin
    $y = 4x - 5$; $y = 4x$; $y - 4x - 1$; parallel lines that intersect the y-axis at different points
    $y = 2x + 1$; $y = 2x - 5$; $y = 2x + 6$; parallel lines that intersect the y-axis at different points
    $y = 4x - 5$; $y = ^-x - 5$; $y = ^-5$; non-parallel lines that intersect the y-axis at -5
    $y = 0$; $y = 1$; $y = ^-5$; y remains a constant regardless of the value of x, forming a horizontal line through y-axis

Exploring Families of Graphs

Answer the questions.

Graph A Graph B   Graph C

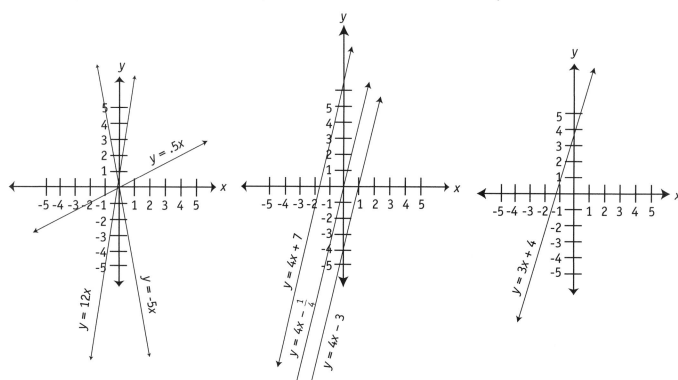

❶ Which graph shows lines with
   the same slope? Explain.

❷ Which graph shows lines that all have equations of the form $y = mx + 4$? Explain.

❸ On which graph do all lines pass through the
   origin (0,0)? Explain why they do so.

**Graph each equation. Determine the slope
and y-intercept for each line.**

❹ $y = {}^-2x + 3$

❺ $y = \frac{2}{3}x - 2$

❻ $y = x + 2$

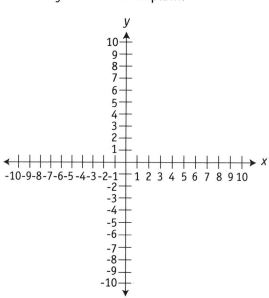

Standard 2 Algebra

Exploring Families of Graphs

Write an additional equation that has a similar characteristic to the equations in each series. Tell why your equation fits.

1 $y = {}^-5x$; $y = {}^-x$; $y = {}^-\frac{2}{3}x$; $y = {}^-2.5x$

2 $y = 0.4x + 8$; $y = 0.4x - 2$; $y = 0.4x = \frac{2}{3}$; $y = 0.4x - 2.5$

3 $y = \frac{1}{2}x$; $y = 2.75x$; $y = {}^-3.5x$; $y = 10x$

4 $y = {}^-x + 5$; $y = {}^-0.5x + 5$; $y = {}^-3x + 5$; $y = {}^-1.5x + 5$

Write an equation that produces:

5 A line parallel to $y = 2x - 1$

6 A line parallel to $y = {}^-x + 5$ passing through the origin.

7 A line parallel to $y = \frac{1}{2}x - 3$ with y-intercept of 8

8 A line with slope of 5 and y-intercept of $^-4$

9 A line with slope of $^-3$ and y-intercept of 7

10 A line that is not parallel to $y = {}^-x + 9$

11 Use the equations listed to make groups of at least 3 equations that have a similar characteristic. Describe the characteristic.

$y = {}^-3x + 6$ $y = {}^-3x$

$y = 4x - 5$ $y = 2x + 1$

$y = 4x$ $y = 2x - 5$

$y = \frac{1}{2}x + 1$ $y = {}^-x - 5$

$y = 2x + 6$ $y = \frac{1}{2}x$

$y = {}^-x$ $y = 3x$

$y = 1$ $y = 4x + 1$

$y = {}^-5$ $y = 0$

Solving One-Step Multiplication and Division Equations

Introduction

Objective → Students will solve multiplication and division equations involving fractions and decimals.

Context → This lesson comes early in a unit on solving equations. Students have solved simple equations with all operations and have worked with addition/subtraction equations involving fractions, decimals, and integers. They will go on to solve two-step equations and use equations in problem solving.

Solving One-Step Multiplication and Division Equations
•••

Learn

In $2\frac{2}{3}$ months Ms. Tanzer has driven her new car 3,672 miles. She wants to find the average number of miles she has driven each month.

She uses m to stand for the average number of miles she drives in a month.

She then sets up the equation $2\frac{2}{3}m = 3,672$.

Ms. Tanzer can find the average number of miles per month by multiplying both sides of the equation by the reciprocal of $2\frac{2}{3}$.

To find the reciprocal, she changes $2\frac{2}{3}$ to $\frac{8}{3}$.

$\frac{3}{8}$ is the reciprocal of $\frac{8}{3}$.

$\frac{3}{8} = \left(\frac{8}{3}\right) = m = \frac{3}{8}(3,672)$

$m = 1,377$ miles.

Other Examples

A. $40r = 910$

      $\left(\frac{1}{40}\right)40r = \left(\frac{1}{40}\right)910$

           $r = 22.75$

B. $\frac{1}{5}y = {}^-15$

      $\left(\frac{5}{1}\right)\frac{1}{5}y = \left(\frac{5}{1}\right)({}^-15)$

         $y = {}^-75$

Write

1. Describe how to find the reciprocal of a fraction. Use words and symbols.
2. Describe how to find the reciprocal of an integer.

Try

What must be done to solve each equation?

1. $6a = 18$
2. ${}^-6a = 18$
3. $w - 4 = 5$
4. $1.4z = 31.5$
5. $2\frac{1}{3}y = 2\frac{1}{3}$
6. $\frac{b}{14} = 5\frac{1}{4}$
7. $\frac{3}{4}a = 24$
8. $1.5x = 60$
9. $1\frac{1}{2}n = 6$

NCTM Process Standards Analysis and Focus

The standards analysis examines how the process standards have been incorporated into the above lesson. By increasing the focus on three of the process standards, a more effective and meaningful lesson can be presented. The suggestions offered can help you to think about how this might be accomplished.

Communication The exercises in the lesson do not encourage a sharing of ideas.

Suggestion → Have students examine various equations to discuss what they represent and suggest solution methods. Understanding what an equation represents will help students recognize the steps needed to solve it. Detailing a solution procedure will help clarify thinking and reinforce procedure.

Practice

1. $3d = 9$

2. $\frac{1}{4}x = 8$

3. $\frac{3}{5}n = \frac{3}{4}$

4. $0.4a = 7.3$

5. $\frac{2}{3}n = 2\frac{5}{6}$

6. $1\frac{3}{4}t = \frac{3}{8}$

7. $1.4m = 21$

8. $21.7 = 3.1y$

9. $28.3 = \frac{n}{2}$

10. $6r = 31.8$

11. $^-7a = 497$

12. $12w = 14.4$

13. $^-5n = ^-23$

14. $\frac{5}{8}f = 1$

15. $^-18 = 1.2z$

16. $^-6 = 1.2f$

17. $\frac{4}{5} + f = 9$

18. $\frac{23}{11} - x = 12$

19. $3\frac{5}{6} + m = 7$

20. $5 = 2\frac{2}{3} + a$

21. $4\frac{2}{5}x = 22$

22. $1 = 3\frac{3}{4}f$

23. $6.2 = b + 6.2$

24. $^-6.2 = b + 6.2$

25. $\frac{3}{5}x = 3\frac{3}{5}$

26. $\frac{7}{8}x = 49$

27. $4\frac{1}{2} = \frac{3}{8}y$

28. $^-\frac{1}{3}w = 2\frac{2}{3}$

Complete each sentence.

29. A(n) _____ is a statement that contains an equal sign.

30. The _____ of 5 is $\frac{1}{5}$.

31. To solve $4 + 24 \div 6 \times 16$, the first operation is _____.

32. To solve $11 - (6 + 2) \times 5$, the first operation is _____.

Problem Solving

33. Gerri's car is 72 times larger than the model. The car is 17 feet long. How long is the model?

34. Penny used $2\frac{1}{2}$ times the amount of ingredients called for in the biscuit recipe. She made 30 biscuits. How many biscuits does the regular recipe make?

35. An object on the moon weighs about $\frac{1}{6}$ what it weighs on Earth. A moon rock weighs 24.8 pounds on the moon. Estimate its weight on Earth.

Suggestion → Provide opportunities throughout the lesson for students to describe how they will solve equations, and have them justify their approach. This will help develop a stronger understanding of the solution process. Having students check their answers by using substitution will allow them to verify their solutions.

Connections The lesson shows how to solve an equation using the reciprocal method but does not connect that method to inverse operations.

Suggestion → Review using inverse operations to solve addition/subtraction equations containing decimals, fractions, and integers. Help students make connections to prior knowledge of solving equations involving multiplication and division. Making these connections

will help students see the consistency of the procedures employed.

Reasoning and Proof The lesson asks students to write a rule explaining how to find the reciprocal of a fraction or integer. Students are also asked to explain how to solve certain equations. At the end of the lesson, students are asked to explain why different forms of the same expression are equal.

Problem Solving Word problems in the lesson allow students to apply the procedures learned but do not actually involve problem solving.

Representation Examples illustrate the reciprocal method for solving equations containing multiplication by fractions. Equations with decimals are not represented. Only one approach to thinking about the equations is shown.

The teaching plan that follows shows how the suggestions for increasing the focus on the process standards can be implemented.

Revised Teaching Plan

BEGIN THE LESSON BY HAVING STUDENTS solve simple equations such as $3y = 81$ or $\frac{n}{7} = 4$. Connecting to prior knowledge of solving equations will give students a base on which to build and help them recognize that procedures they have learned are applicable in similar situations, regardless of the set of numbers involved.

Ask students to give reasons for their choice of solution method and have them explain their steps as they write the solution on the board. Encourage students who used different methods to share their thinking. Point out similarities and/or connections between methods.

If no student describes using inverse operations as a solution method, present this approach. Emphasize that using inverse operations to solve these equations follows the same line of thinking they applied when they solved equations such as $25 + y = 239$ or $m - 64 = 117$. If necessary, quickly review the steps for solving addition and/or subtraction equations. Making these connections will help students recognize the consistency of mathematical ideas and procedures.

CONTINUE BY PRESENTING A PROBLEM SITUATION EASILY solved by employing strategies such as applying number sense, drawing a picture, or using guess and check. *Tim filled $2\frac{1}{2}$ scrapbook pages with photos. Each filled page had the same number of photos. There were 15 photos in all. How many photos are on each page?*

Allow a few minutes for students to think about and suggest ways to solve the problem. Encourage the use of algebraic representation. *What math sentence or equation would represent this problem?* Students should be able to respond $2\frac{1}{2} n = 15$. Some students may offer $2.5n = 15$. Accept both forms and have students compare the equations. Proceeding in this way with a simple problem will reinforce students' understanding of equations and show them that the numbers involved do not change how they translate the situation.

f.y.i.

In addition or subtraction, using the inverse yields 0, the identity element for addition and subtraction. In multiplication and division, using the inverse yields 1, the identity element for those operations. Using the multiplicative inverse, or reciprocal, also yields a coefficient of 1. Both methods produce the same result—isolating the variable on one side of the equation.

ASK STUDENTS TO APPLY WHAT THEY KNOW about solving equations to the equation $2\frac{1}{2}n = 15$. *What does the variable represent in this equation?* (The number of photos on a full page) *What operation is being performed on (what is being done to) the variable in this equation?* (Multiplication. The variable is being multiplied by 2.)

When a number was added to the variable, we subtracted. When a number was subtracted from the variable, we added. What should we do when a number multiplies the variable? (Divide) *Why?* (Multiplication and division are inverse operations.) *What is the purpose of using the inverse operation?* (It undoes or negates the operation.) This discussion will help students understand that the solution to many equations begins by identifying an operation and its inverse.

CONTINUE TO DEVELOP THE STEPS needed to solve the equation. Write $2\frac{1}{2}n = 15$ and $2\frac{1}{2} \times n = 15$ on the board. Ask students to compare the two equations and verify that they both have the same meaning. Then show both sides of the equations being divided by $2\frac{1}{2}$. Emphasize that the same operation must be performed on both sides of the equation.

$$2\tfrac{1}{2}n = 15 \qquad\qquad 2\tfrac{1}{2} \times n = 15$$

$$\frac{2\tfrac{1}{2}n}{2\tfrac{1}{2}} = \frac{15}{2\tfrac{1}{2}} \qquad (2\tfrac{1}{2} \times n) \div 2\tfrac{1}{2} = 15 \div 2\tfrac{1}{2}$$

Invite students to supply the steps required to solve these two forms of the division problem. Students should explain that they would rename the mixed number $2\frac{1}{2}$ to an improper fraction of $\frac{5}{2}$. Enlist students' help as you rewrite each equation to show the renaming, solving, and then the checking of the answer using substitution.

Ask students to examine the solutions on the board to see if they can determine a shortcut for solving the equations. Point out that while the solutions started with division, they ended with multiplication. Introduce the reciprocal method. Connect both sides of the original equation multiplied by the reciprocal of the fraction with the final step of the solution using inverse operations.

NEXT, HAVE STUDENTS EXPLAIN the solution steps for the same problem expressed in decimal form, $2.5n = 15$. This reworking reinforces the consistency of solution methods.

Present a division equation that contains integers, such as $n \div 45 = {}^{-}12$. Ask students to explain what the equation represents, and have them identify the operation involved. *Will* n *be positive or negative?* Making connections to the rules for multiplication and division with integers will remind students to think about the sign for the value of n. Then have students work the problem and share their solution methods, prompting them to offer clarification and explanation when necessary. In this way, you can assess their understanding of the lesson.

What Might Happen . . . What to Do

When solving an equation such as $-\frac{2}{3}n = 8$, students may not consider the sign and use $\frac{3}{2}$ as the reciprocal instead of $-\frac{3}{2}$. Review integer multiplication, reminding students that multiplying like signs yields a positive product and multiplying unlike signs yields a negative. Also review reciprocals, reminding students that multiplying a number by its reciprocal should result in a product of 1. *Is the sentence* $-\frac{2}{3} \times \frac{3}{2} = 1$ *true?* (No.) *Why?* ($-\frac{2}{3} \times \frac{3}{2} = {}^{-}1$) *What must* $-\frac{2}{3}$ *be multiplied by to get a product of* 1? Provide additional examples as practice.

If time allows, have students work individually or in pairs to solve a few additional problems. Instruct them to record their steps.

Student Pages

Students should now be ready to complete exercises similar to those on the reduced student pages.

Assessment

As students discussed what different equations represented and the steps involved in solving them, there were ample opportunities to assess their understanding of the concepts and procedures.

NCTM Standards Summary

Students participated in discussions about what equations represent and communicated their ideas about how to solve equations. By listening to one another's ideas, students had a chance to recognize that there may be several approaches to solving a problem. Reviewing the use of inverse operations to solve addition and subtraction equations allowed students to connect that method to solving multiplication and division equations. Another important connection was made as students solved equations containing fractions, decimals, and integers by following the same basic procedures. Asking students to provide the reasoning behind their solution steps gave them an opportunity to clarify their understanding of the solution process. Finally, generalizing a shortcut method to multiply by the reciprocal allowed them to see the relationship between inverse operations and the reciprocal method.

Standard 3 **Geometry**

AT THE EIGHTH GRADE LEVEL, geometry includes work with parallel and perpendicular, congruence and similarity, and covering surfaces. Our lessons are derived from these important topics, and include a lesson on identifying parallel and perpendicular lines, a lesson on understanding similarity, a lesson that explores tessellations, and a lesson on congruent figures.

Three lessons model how the process standards can be used to teach content. A fourth lesson is a hypothetical textbook lesson that we have revised to be more standards based. These four lessons do not represent the entire curriculum, but rather provide glimpses of how, with a more concentrated effort to incorporate the process standards, better mathematics teaching and learning can be achieved.

One lesson we have chosen is one in which students draw lines and determine whether they are parallel, perpendicular, or neither. Instead of just being given the definitions in terms of slope, students use reasoning and proof, representation, and communication to broaden their knowledge to include more about how the geometric relationships parallel and perpendicular can translate to analytic relationships.

Another lesson we have chosen is one in which students discover the properties of similar figures. Students are generally given a definition and asked to apply it to pairs of shapes. In this standards-based lesson, students use a protractor and ruler to investigate for themselves what makes figures similar.

A third lesson that we have chosen is one that explores whether or not certain geometric shapes will tessellate. This lesson is driven by the process standards of problem solving and reasoning and proof, as students work to decide which regular polygons will tessellate. Students try to generalize from their results in order to predict whether a certain figure will tessellate or not.

The hypothetical textbook lesson that we have chosen to revise has students use transformations to show that two figures are congruent. Through better incorporation of the process standards of reasoning and proof, representation, and communication, students will predict the vertices of a congruent figure after a transformation. Students' analytical thinking and visualization skills are both explored during this lesson.

Standard 3 Lessons

Identifying Parallel and Perpendicular Lines

Understanding Similarity

Exploring Tessellations

Investigating Congruent Figures

Identifying Parallel and Perpendicular Lines

Introduction

Objective → Given the coordinates of two points on each of two lines in a coordinate plane, students will be able to draw the lines and determine whether the lines are parallel, perpendicular, or neither.

Context → This lesson comes towards the end of a chapter on coordinate graphing. Students are familiar with the meaning of slope and methods for computing slope. They may have had practice in evaluating the relationships formed by a transversal and parallel lines.

NCTM Standards Focus

The work in this lesson illustrates how geometric relationships can be translated into analytical relationships. This helps students discern how alternate representations of the same concept can lead to a new level of understanding. Through an ongoing sharing and refining of ideas and results, students check and test their solutions. The activities assist students in recognizing the difference between verification and mathematical proof.

Reasoning and Proof Students use their understanding of basic geometric definitions to formulate methods for determining whether two lines, graphed on a coordinate plane, are parallel, perpendicular, or neither. Students form and test a hypothesis, and state their observations as a general rule.

Representation By representing lines on a coordinate plane and analyzing the coordinates of points on the lines, students discover new methods for identifying parallel and perpendicular lines.

Communication Throughout the lesson, students explain their ideas and observations about the lines they draw. These opportunities for communication help students clarify their thinking and reinforce their skills in formulating precise mathematical concepts.

Teaching Plan

Materials → Student pages 74–75; graph paper; straightedge; protractor

BEGIN THE LESSON by reviewing the ways that two lines in the same plane can be related. Ask students to jot down how they can determine whether two lines are parallel. Discuss the relevance and accuracy of their statements. Students may state that two lines are parallel if:

- they never meet no matter how far they are extended;
- they are always equidistant;
- they have no points in common.

Be sure to challenge any erroneous or incomplete definitions.

Next, ask students to record how they can determine whether two lines are perpendicular. Students might respond that two lines are perpendicular if:

- they intersect to form 90-degree angles;
- they form perfect corners where they intersect.

Again, discuss their definitions, challenging any that are erroneous.

Remind students that a pair of lines cannot be both parallel and perpendicular, but they can be neither. Ask students to draw a pair of lines that are neither perpendicular nor parallel. Have them explain how they know these lines are neither parallel nor perpendicular. They should respond that the lines intersect, or will intersect, but do not form 90-degree angles.

What Might Happen . . . What to Do

Some students might think that perpendicular lines must be formed by one horizontal and one vertical line. If so, have students use a protractor to create a pair of lines that are perpendicular but not horizontal and vertical. This will help them realize that when they graph lines on the coordinate plane, the lines need not follow the lines of the grid to be perpendicular.

INVOLVE STUDENTS IN A DISCUSSION of methods they could use to decide if two lines drawn on a plane are parallel, perpendicular, or neither. As students describe their methods, ask them to explain the relationships to the basic definitions. For example, to determine parallelism, students might indicate they would try extending the lines to see if they would meet, or measure the distance between the lines at several points to see if it stays constant, or draw a transversal and measure reference angles. Point out that with the exception of measuring angles created by a transversal, none of these methods will absolutely establish parallelism. To determine perpendicularity, students might use a protractor to measure the angles at the intersection, or try to construct a square using the lines as two sides. Students may suggest many other methods, but they should be asked to justify each one.

Explain that today students are going to explore another method for determining parallel and perpendicular lines by representing such lines on a coordinate plane and analyzing the coordinates of points on the lines. Ask students to visualize parallel lines. Point out that parallel lines may be described as "slanting" in the same direction. If two lines do not intersect, they rise and fall at the same rate. *How do we measure this rate?* (By calculating slope) Therefore, it seems reasonable to see if slope will give us some

If students try to check for perpendicularity of the horizontal and vertical pair of lines they drew earlier, they may have a difficult time. The slope of the horizontal line is zero. The slope of the vertical line is undefined. It follows that the slopes of vertical parallel lines will be undefined and the slopes of horizontal parallel lines will be zero. This concept of a zero slope is probably easier for students to grasp because the horizontal line is flat, and has no visible slant, or slope.

information about whether lines are perpendicular or parallel. Ask students to make a hypothesis regarding how the slopes of parallel lines are related.

Give students a sheet of graph paper and have them work individually or in pairs to graph the lines containing each of the following pairs of points.

(1,2) and (1,5); (3,4) and (3,7)   (2,5) and (6,5); (4,8) and (8,8)

In each case, ask if the lines are parallel. *How do you know the lines are parallel?* Since these lines follow grid lines, it is easy to discern that they are parallel. Summarize the results. *If two lines are horizontal or if two lines are vertical, they are parallel.*

Next, have students graph the pair of lines containing the points (1,4) and (6,4), (2,2) and (2,7). Students should see that, since one line is horizontal and one line is vertical, the lines are perpendicular.

Ask students to graph the pair of lines containing the points (2,2) and (4,6); (6,4) and (7,6). Tell students that the lines containing these points are parallel. If necessary, review the calculation of slope, and then ask students to calculate the slopes of the lines. Ask them what they notice about the slopes of each line. (The slopes are equal.) *Does this agree with your original hypothesis?* Have students perform the slope test for pairs of lines containing the following sets of points:

(0,5) and (1,3); (2,4) and (3,2) (Parallel)
(1,6) and (3,4); (0,5) and (2,1) (Not parallel)

TO EXPLORE PERPENDICULAR LINES, have students graph the lines containing the points (2,2) and (4,5); (7,0) and (1,4). Tell students that this pair of lines is perpendicular. Ask them to determine the slopes of the lines. ($\frac{3}{2}$ and $\frac{-2}{3}$) Then ask them to graph the perpendicular lines containing the points (3,2) and (11,8); (3,9) and (9,1). Again, have students determine the slopes of the lines. ($\frac{3}{4}$ and $\frac{-4}{3}$) Ask students to compare the slopes from the two sets of perpendicular lines to see if there is a pattern. Students should notice that the slopes within each set are opposite reciprocals. If they cannot readily see the relationship, ask them to multiply the slopes together. If the lines are perpendicular, the product will be $^-1$. Once students recognize and express the relationship between the slopes of pairs of perpendicular lines, provide a few more sets of points and ask them to determine whether or not the lines are perpendicular.

TO END THE LESSON, bring the class together and summarize the slope tests for parallel and perpendicular lines. Ask students to give their opinions of the advantages of using the slope method over other methods of determining parallel and perpendicular lines.

Assign student pages 74 and 75 for class work or homework.

Student Pages

Student page 74 requires students to graph ordered pairs and determine whether the lines containing the points are perpendicular, parallel, or neither. Student page 75 asks students to use slope (without graphing) to determine whether pairs of lines are perpendicular, parallel, or neither.

Assessment

You had opportunities to assess students as they hypothesized about the slopes of the lines using prior knowledge, and then graphed the lines on coordinate grids. As they calculated and compared the slopes in pairs of lines, you had a chance to observe students' reasoning skills. The review at the end of the lesson allowed you to see if students had formalized the concept of using slope to determine parallelism and perpendicularity.

NCTM Standards Summary

By thinking of ways to show that pairs of lines are perpendicular or parallel, students reinforced their understanding of basic geometric definitions and gained experience formulating mathematical verifications. The explorations in the lesson provided opportunities to generalize results and then apply these generalizations. Students were able to extend their knowledge about line relationships and coordinate graphing. Representing lines on coordinate planes provided students with new tools for determining parallelism and perpendicularity and illustrated how mathematical relationships can be reinterpreted in different contexts. Sharing ideas helped students recognize the usefulness of slope in their work and actively involved them in the process of building their problem-solving skills.

Answers

Page 74
1. perpendicular, slopes 2, $\frac{-1}{2}$
2. neither, slopes $\frac{5}{6}$, 1
3. parallel, slopes $\frac{-1}{3}$
4. neither, slopes $\frac{-1}{2}$, $\frac{7}{4}$

Page 75
1. parallel
2. parallel
3. neither
4. perpendicular
5. perpendicular
6. parallel
7. rectangle, 2 pairs of parallel lines set perpendicular to each other, whose diagonals do not form perpendicular lines, slopes of lines = $\frac{-1}{3}$, 3, slopes of diagonals = $^-7$, 1
8. square, 2 pairs of parallel lines set perpendicular to each other, whose diagonals are also perpendicular to each other, slopes of lines = $\frac{1}{2}$, $^-2$, slopes of diagonals = 3, $\frac{-1}{3}$
9. parallelogram, 2 sets of parallel lines, not perpendicular to each other, slopes = $^-4$, 3
10. rectangle, 2 pairs of parallel lines set perpendicular to each other, whose diagonals are not perpendicular to each other, slopes of lines = $\frac{1}{2}$, $^-2$, slopes of diagonals = $\frac{4}{3}$, 0

Identifying Parallel and Perpendicular Lines

In numbers 3–6, graph the lines determined by each set of ordered pairs. Determine whether the lines are perpendicular, parallel, or neither.

❶ (1,1), (0,-1); (-8,6), (-2,3)

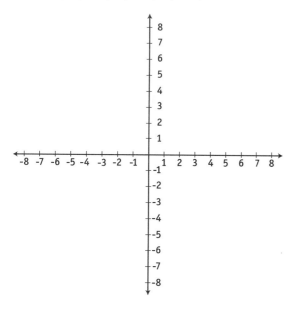

❷ (-3,-2), (3,3); (0,-1), (3,2)

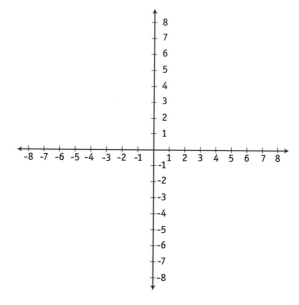

❸ (-4,1), (-1,0); (-1,2), (5,0)

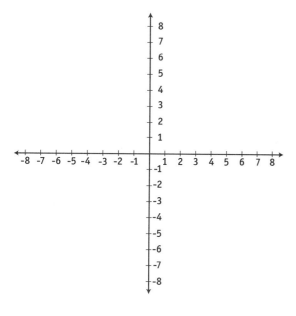

❹ (-4,3), (4,-1); (-2,-2), (2,5)

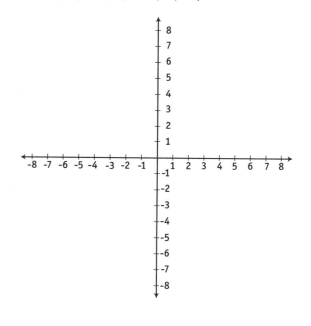

Standard 3 Geometry

Identifying Parallel and Perpendicular Lines

Use slope to determine whether each set of lines is parallel, perpendicular, or neither. Do not graph the lines containing the points.

❶ (7,15), (8,18); (6,6), (8,12)

❷ (5,⁻9), (17,⁻6); (1,7), (5,8)

❸ (⁻1,⁻3), (3,8); (2,1), (7,12)

❹ (⁻2,12), (⁻1,14); (3,13), (5,12)

❺ (4,6), (5,3); (⁻9,4), (⁻6,5)

❻ (3,13), (7,15); (⁻12,10), (⁻2,15)

Name the figure formed by each set of coordinates. Use slope to confirm your observations.

❼

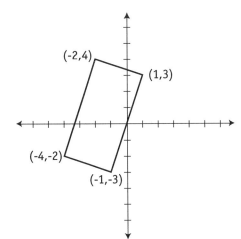

❽

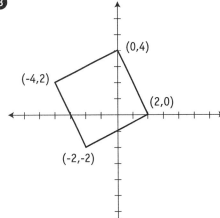

❾

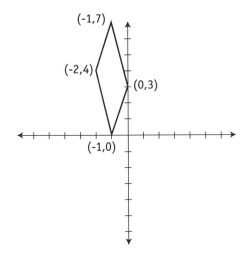

❿

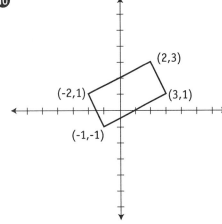

Understanding Similarity

Introduction

Objective → Students will discover properties of similar figures.

Context → Students have measured angles using a protractor and measured length using a centimeter ruler. Students know ratios and equivalent ratios. Students will go on to learn more about similar and congruent figures.

NCTM Standards Focus

Often the concept of similarity is presented as a definition with illustrations and students are asked to apply the definition to a series of shapes. Students learn the definitions but they may fail to see the deeper underlying connections between geometry and the rest of mathematics. In particular, they may fail to fully understand the proportional relationship between the corresponding sides of two similar geometric shapes. By giving students the opportunity to help construct their own definitions before traditional definitions are presented, they will have a solid experiential base to help them remember and apply the content of this lesson to their later explorations in geometry.

Reasoning and Proof Students reason about what makes a triangle similar to another triangle. They study and construct triangles with straightedge, protractor, and ruler to demonstrate their thinking.

Representation Students work with representations of triangles to determine similarity. They also make representations of similar triangles.

Communication Students present similar shapes to each other and describe why they are similar. Students sort among several triangles to find the similar triangles.

Teaching Plan

Materials → Student pages 80–81; overhead transparency of student page 80 (optional); centimeter rulers; straightedge; protractor

HAND OUT STUDENT PAGE 80 and show it on the overhead. There are four triangles on the page, two of which are similar. Ask students what the triangles on the page have in common. Students may notice that two of the triangles look more alike than the other two triangles. Triangles *DEF* and *GHI* are similar. If they do not notice this, ask students if they see two triangles that look more alike than the others. Have students look for the two triangles and see if they can tell why the triangles are more alike.

Tell students you want them to make a chart of some the characteristics of each triangle. Tell them they will be trying to find out what makes some triangles more like others. Discuss with them what should be on the chart. The most important points are the measure of each angle and the length of each side. Have students make a chart for each triangle and find this information.

After they finish the chart, have them compare the information for each triangle with the other triangles, looking for similarities.

After students have found the information, get them back together and discuss what they found. All measures are approximate.

f.y.i.

Some students may suggest area as a characteristic. It is probably better to help students focus on just sides and angles. Area may make things more complicated and more difficult to see the relationships.

Triangle ABC			
Side	Length	Angle	Measure
AB	4 cm	BAC	27°
BC	4 cm	ABC	127°
CA	7 cm	BCA	26°

Triangle DEF			
Side	Length	Angle	Measure
DE	3 cm	FDE	52°
EF	4 cm	DEF	90°
FD	5 cm	EFD	28°

Triangle GHI			
Side	Length	Angle	Measure
GH	6 cm	IGH	52°
HI	8 cm	GHI	90°
IG	10 cm	HIG	28°

Triangle JKL			
Side	Length	Angle	Measure
JK	3 cm	LJK	70°
KL	4 cm	JKL	70°
LJ	4 cm	KLJ	40°

Discuss with students what they found. One thing students are likely to notice is that triangles *DEF* and *GHI* have the same angle measures. Because of the inaccuracies of measurement, students may have slightly different results for the angles. This can be a good time to briefly discuss the inaccuracies of measurement.

Ask students if they can see any relationships with the sides. Students might notice the relationships within a triangle. For example, the ratio of the lengths of sides *DE* and *EF* is 3 to 4, the ratio of *EF* and *FD* is 4 to 5. The same relationship exists between the corresponding sides of the triangle *GHI*. The ratio of *GH* to *HI* is 6 to 8 or 3 to 4. The ratio of *HI* to *IG* is 8 to 10 or 4 to 5. Students can also see that there is a relationship between the sides of the triangles. Each side of *GHI* is twice the length of the corresponding sides of triangle *DEF*.

Students should see that these relationships do not hold for any of the other triangles. If students have not already suggested it, tell them that these are *similar* triangles. Have them review how they can identify similar triangles.

Now ask students how many triangles similar to triangles *DEF* and *GHI* could be made. Have them support their ideas with examples. Students should be able to see that they can make an infinite number. Tell students

f.y.i.

Some students may think that you can make different triangles with the same side measurements. If you think the class needs to see this, have them cut strips of paper 3 cm, 4 cm, and 5 cm. Ask them to try and make different triangles with their strips. They will see they can only make one triangle.

What Might Happen . . . What to Do

Some students might have trouble understanding there must be a relationship between all the sides. They may see that triangle *DEF* and *JKL* are close in that they have sides of 3, 4, and 5 and 3, 4, and 4. Make an extra copy of the student page and have students cut out the triangles and place them on top of one another. In doing so they can see how *DEF* fits with *GHI* and that *JKL* almost fits with *DEF* but not quite.

---

that the class is going to attempt to have each pair of students try to make a different triangle that is similar to the two triangles. Discuss with students how they could make sure that each pair of students made a similar but different triangle. Let students try a method they think would work. One method that will work is to have each pair use a different factor to change the length of the sides. If you use this method, be sure some students make smaller triangles, using a factor such as 0.5. Have students make and then display all their triangles along with the original ones.

Now have students take either triangle *ABC* or *JKL* and make a similar triangle. When they are done, discuss why they are similar and display them. End the lesson with a review and definition of similarity.

Extension

If you have time or want to give students a project, have them make similar figures using other polygons. Ask them which polygons would be the easiest to do. They may mention that squares and rhombi are very easy since they are all similar. Discuss with them why this is so. They should see that the relationship between the sides in the square and the rhombi are always the same, since the sides are always the same.

You may wish to assign student page 81 to be done in class or for homework.

Student Pages

Student page 80 provides the triangles for the lesson activity. Student page 81 pictures several triangles, asks students to make similar triangles, and to tell why they are similar.

Assessment

During the activity and discussions you had an opportunity to assess students' understanding of how to compare the angles and lengths of sides of triangles. You were also able to see whether they could identify the factors that make two triangles similar and if they could make a similar triangle. The student page gave you the opportunity to judge what they could do on their own.

NCTM Standards Summary

This lesson asked students to see if they could determine what made triangles similar by studying representations and using reasoning skills to compare triangles. When students found relationships between triangles, they communicated these with other students and then tested these ideas by attempting to make similar figures. Once they had an understanding of similar figures, they discussed how many similar figures could be made and experimented with how to make sure their figures were different. Finally, they used this information to look at other triangles and figures.

Answers

Page 80
There are no answers.

Page 81
Answer will vary.

Understanding Similarity

Use these triangles for the class activity.

❶ Triangle *ABC*

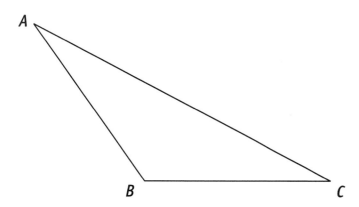

❷ Triangle *DEF*

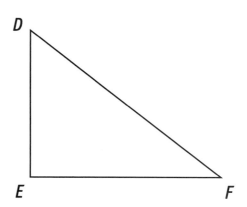

❸ Triangle *GHI*

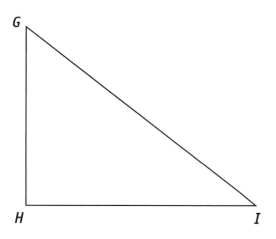

❹ Triangle *JKL*

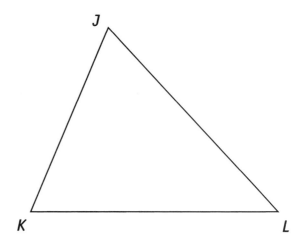

Standard 3 Geometry

Understanding Similarity

On another sheet of paper draw a triangle that is similar to each triangle on this page. Explain what you did to make the similar triangle.

① Triangle *PQR*

② Triangle *STU*

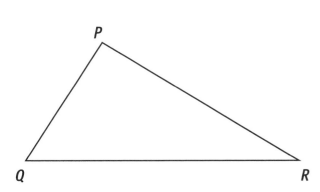
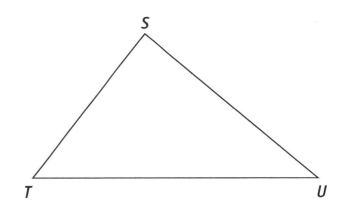

③ Triangle *VWX*

④ Triangle *DEF*

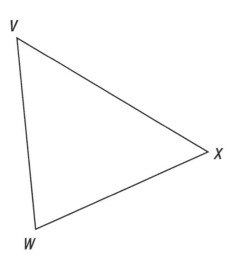
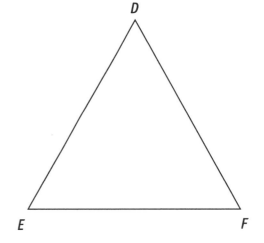

Exploring Tessellations

Introduction

Objective → Students will be able to determine which of a set of given regular geometric shapes will tessellate.

Context → Students have worked extensively with two-dimensional geometric shapes. They are comfortable with finding angle measures and will use this knowledge to determine which of a series of geometric shapes will tessellate.

NCTM Standards Focus

The study of tessellations provides students with both a mathematical foundation for future geometric studies and an example of how mathematics ties to the real world. In this standards-based lesson, students explore how mathematics forms the underpinnings of tessellations and apply their findings as they create their own tessellating patterns.

Problem Solving Students manipulate regular polygons to determine whether they will tessellate. They explore changes that can be made to figures that tessellate to create their own variations in tessellating patterns.

Reasoning and Proof Students determine relationships that are needed for figures to tessellate. They apply this understanding as they explain whether new figures will tessellate.

Connections Students connect knowledge of polygons, angle measurement, and transformations to tessellations. Connections will be made between this interesting area of mathematics and the realm of art and design.

Teaching Plan

Materials → Student pages 86–87; scissors; rulers; 2" × 2" cardstock squares or index cards; tape; 11" × 17" white paper; colored pencils

Preparation → Prior to the lesson, duplicate enough copies of student page 86 to supply each student with at least a dozen of each shape to use in their explorations. If possible, use stiff paper or cardstock to make copies. Also, cut out a set of shapes to use for demonstration purposes.

BEGIN BY TELLING STUDENTS that in this lesson they will explore tiling a plane surface with regular geometric shapes. Display the shapes that students will work with on the overhead projector. Take a few minutes to have students identify each of the shapes and determine that they are regular polygons. *What is a regular polygon?* (One that has congruent sides and congruent angles.) *How can we determine whether these figures are regular polygons?* (By measuring their sides and angles, or by placing one over another and rotating them to see that sides and angles are congruent.)

Explain that tiling is often accomplished using a single shape. Congruent polygons are fitted together so there is no overlapping and no spaces are left uncovered. The resulting pattern is called a *tessellation*. Ask students to tell where they have seen repeated patterns of a shape, or tessellations, used to cover a surface. Expect a range of answers; the most common examples are tiling on walls and floors.

ARRANGE STUDENTS IN GROUPS OF 3–4 and distribute copies of student page 86. Explain to students that they are to cut out their shapes and share them with one another. Groups are to explore which of the six shapes can be used repeatedly to tessellate a plane. Emphasize that in order to tessellate, a figure must be able to cover a surface completely leaving no gaps or empty spaces.

Allow about 10–15 minutes for groups to work on this task. Then hold a class discussion and ask each group to briefly share the results of their exploration. Students should be able to identify that when using a single shape, the equilateral triangle, the square, and the regular hexagon could be tessellated, but the regular pentagon, the regular heptagon, and the regular octagon could not be tessellated. If students suggest other results, ask them to use the overhead projector to show their solutions and have the class determine whether they are correct.

Explain to students that they have determined which figures would tessellate by experimental trial. Encourage them to share any insights they might have gained during their explorations that helped them to determine whether a figure could be tessellated.

HAVE STUDENTS PLACE FOUR of their squares together to form another square as you draw the diagram shown on the overhead. Focus on the number of degrees where the 4 corners come together. Students should see that since each angle of a square is 90°, the total measure around the point where the four vertices meet is 360°.

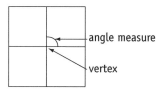

Examine angle relationships for the other figures that tessellated. *How were the triangles arranged in order to tessellate the plane?* (Vertices of 6 triangles met together, or, vertices of 3 triangles met to form a straight line, and straight lines met.) *What is the measure of each vertex of the triangle? Explain how you know.* (Each vertex is 60°. The three angles of any triangle equal 180°. In a regular triangle, the angles are congruent. 180° ÷ 3 = 60°.) *How many degrees are there where 6 triangles come together?* (360°) *What about the straight lines?* (Straight lines are 180°. Two straight lines together are 360°.)

Repeat the same line of questioning for the regular hexagon. Students should be able to tell that three hexagons fit together around a point, making a total of 360°, and since the vertices are congruent, each angle of the hexagon must be equal 120°.

Summarize the angle relationships by explaining that there are two constant mathematical conclusions for regular geometric figures that tessellate. Present the following on the overhead:

Conclusions for Regular Polygons that will Tessellate

Conclusion 1
The sum of the angle measures at any vertex in a tessellation must be 360°.

Conclusion 2
When dividing 360° by the angle measure of a regular polygon, the quotient will be a whole number.

NEXT, HAVE STUDENTS LOOK at the regular polygons they found would not tessellate. Have students determine the angle measurement of each of the figures. Demonstrate how to draw diagonals from one vertex to subdivide a polygon into triangles. Knowing that each triangle has 180°, students should be able to find the total number of degrees for each figure. Dividing the total degrees by the number of congruent angles in the figure will give the measure of each angle. Students should quickly find that the figures that did not tessellate do not meet the conditions listed for regular polygons that will tessellate.

Challenge students to apply their understanding of Conclusion 2 to determine whether a regular 10-sided polygon (decagon) or 12-sided polygon (dodecagon) can be used to tessellate a plane. Explain that although some figures will not tessellate on their own, they can be combined with other figures to form tessellations. Encourage students to experiment with the different shapes, paying special attention to the number of degrees in the angles as they combine shapes.

Distribute student page 87, 2" × 2" cardstock or index cards, scissors, and tape. Explain to students that the diagram on the student page shows how to apply a slide or translation on a figure to create a new shape that will tessellate. Walk through each of the steps with students to make sure they see what was done to create the new figure to be tessellated. Emphasize that when the slide or translation is applied, the piece being moved should be positioned at exactly the same location on the opposite side. This precision with measurement is what will allow the figure to tessellate.

Have students apply slides or translations to their cards to create their own shapes. Instruct them to first draw, then cut a shape from one side and slide it to the opposite side. Suggest that they measure to ensure proper placement and tape the cut piece into place. Students who want to apply another slide should repeat the process. When they think their shape is ready to tessellate, suggest students do a trial run on scratch paper. If their figure works, they are ready to create a tessellation drawing.

Conclude the lesson by providing unlined 11" × 17" paper to students on which they can create a tessellation. They can use the figure they created or create a new figure to tessellate. Encourage students to add color to their completed tessellation. Finished works should be displayed.

Student Pages

Student page 86 consists of various regular geometric shapes for students to cut out and use in class. Student page 87 shows the steps for using translations to create a figure from a square that will tessellate.

Assessment

You were able to assess students' ability to identify shapes that would tessellate as they explored with regular polygons. As they discussed their findings, you could evaluate their understanding of the factors involved in tessellating regular polygons. Their completed tessellation drawings provided further evidence of their understanding of the lesson concepts and their ability to apply them.

NCTM Standards Summary

In this lesson, students applied problem-solving strategies as they explored regular geometric shapes to identify those that would tessellate a plane. Reasoning was involved as students connected their knowledge of geometric figures and angle measurement to determine the characteristics of figures that would tessellate. Connections were also made to real world applications as students discussed tiling and created art.

f.y.i.

The task of completing their own tessellation will take longer than a class period. It is appropriate to introduce this at the close of this lesson and assign the bulk of the task for homework. Most students will find this a unique and enjoyable homework assignment.

Answers

Page 86
Student manipulatives—no answers required.

Page 87
Students' figures and tessellations will vary.

Exploring Tessellations

Cut out and manipulate each of the figures below to find out which ones will tessellate.

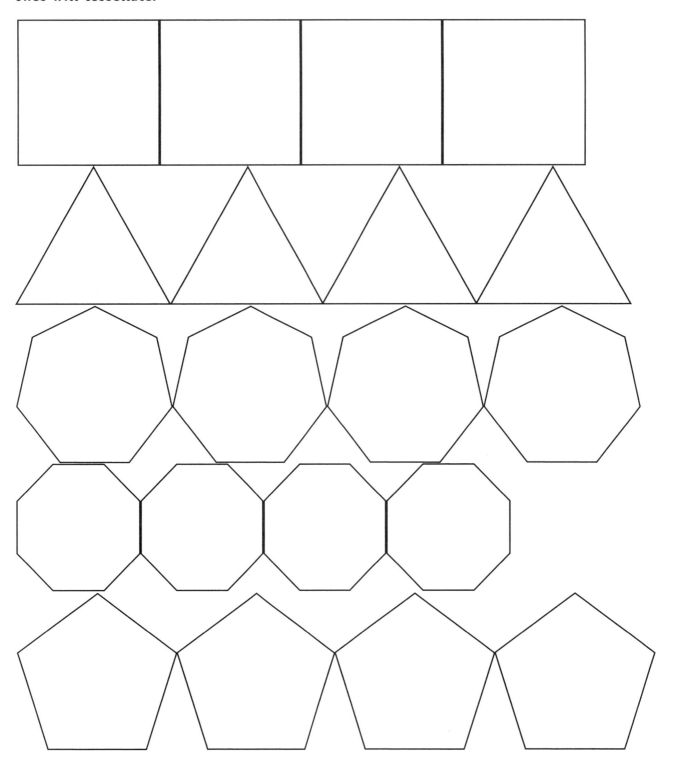

Standard 3 Geometry

Exploring Tessellations

Review the steps below for using translations to create a figure that tessellates.
Make your own unique figure and complete a tessellation. Start with a 2" × 2" square.

Tessellation

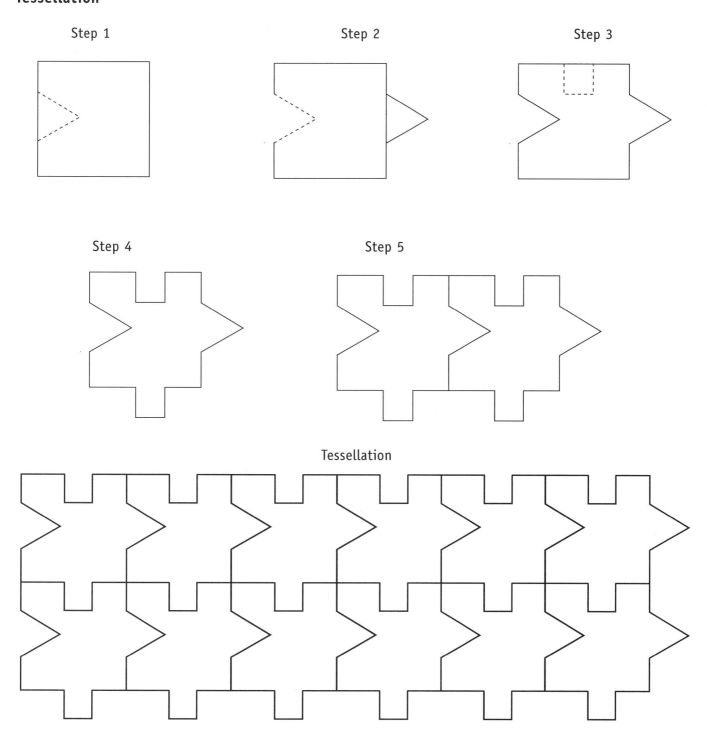

Step 1

Step 2

Step 3

Step 4

Step 5

Tessellation

Investigating Congruent Figures

Introduction

Objective → Students will recognize congruent figures and identify transformations that move one figure to another.

Context → This lesson occurs mid-unit. Students have studied translations (slides), reflections, rotations, and symmetry. They will go on to construct congruent line segments, angles, and triangles.

Investigating Congruent Figures

When two figures are exactly the same they are congruent.

Congruent figures are the same shape and size.

Which two figures below are congruent?

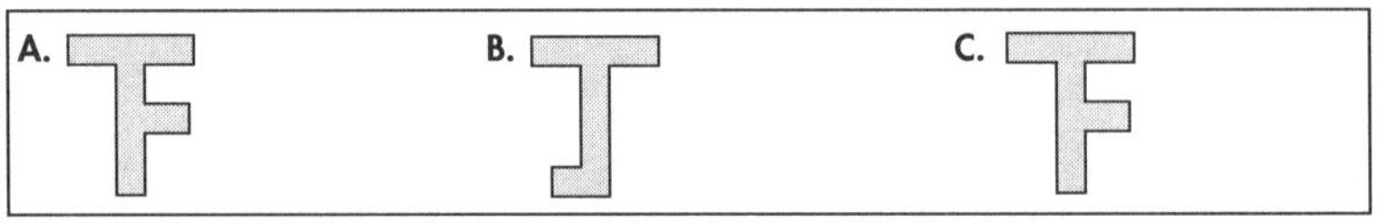

If a figure is a translation of another figure, then the two figures are congruent.

Which figure is a translation of figure D?

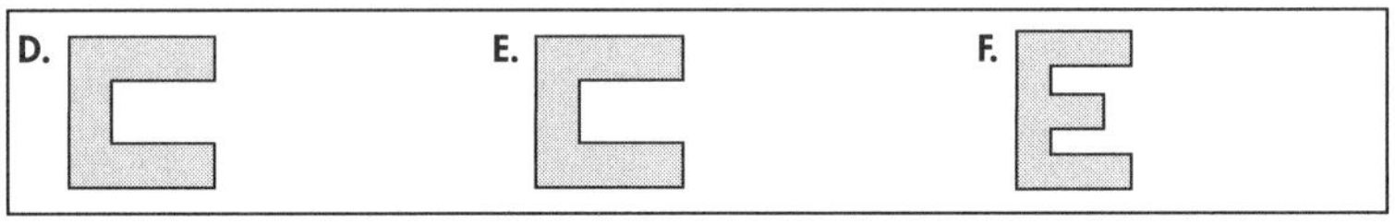

If a figure is a reflection of another figure, then the two figures are congruent.

Which figure is a reflection of figure G?

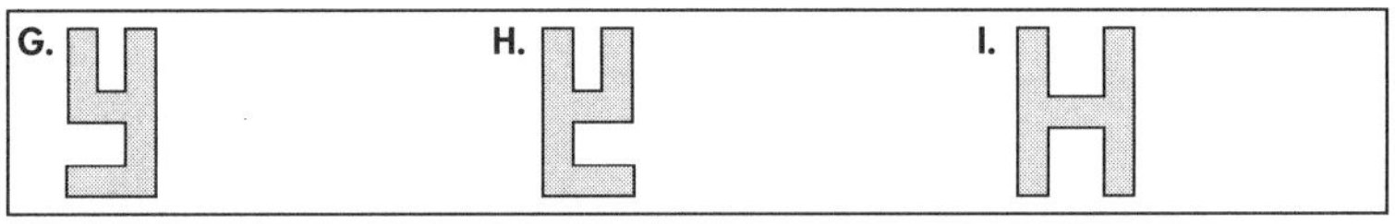

If a figure is a rotation of another figure, then the two figures are congruent.

Which figure is a rotation of figure J.

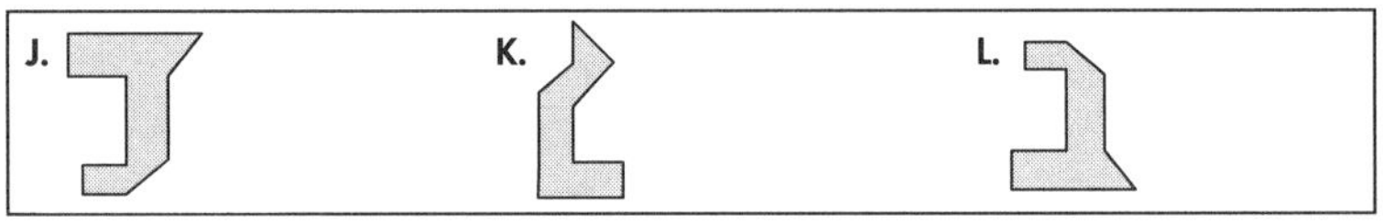

NCTM Process Standards Analysis and Focus

The standards analysis examines how the process standards have been incorporated into the above lesson. By increasing the focus on three of the process standards, a more effective and meaningful lesson can be presented. The suggestions offered can help you to think about how this might be accomplished.

Reasoning and Proof The lesson poses several questions that require students to think about the meaning of congruence and apply their knowledge to identify congruent figures. Only one question is offered that asks students to explain this thinking or how to show that their answer is correct.

Suggestion → Having students explain the thinking they use to identify

· ·

Practice

Tell whether or not these figures are congruent.

1.

2.

3.

4.

Use dot paper. Draw a reflection of each figure.

5.

6.

Problem Solving

7. Rectangles *ABCD* and *EFGH* are congruent. Find the coordinates for points *C*, *D*, *E*, and *F*.

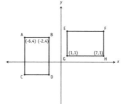

8. On a piece of graph paper, draw a rectangle that is congruent to rectangle *ABCE*. Make sure one vertex is at point ($^-$2, $^-$1).

congruent figures will focus attention on those properties that are, or are not, relevant to congruence. Instruct students to prove or disprove congruence by actually manipulating shapes. Have students use a coordinate plane to transform figures and compare vertices. Then ask students to make predictions about further transformations. This will enhance their ability to reason analytically and formulate generalizations.

Representation Students examine pictures of geometric shapes to determine congruence.

Suggestion → Provide activities in which students perform transformations with shapes they have created. This will develop their ability to recognize changes in orientation. Encourage students to challenge one another to identify drawings that may or may not be transformations of congruent

figures to reinforce their understanding of congruence.

Communication Because most questions can be answered in one or two words, opportunities for discussion are limited.

Suggestion → Initiate discussions that require students to explain their thinking and make generalizations or predictions. Considering factors that determine congruence and communicating about how different transformations affect the appearance of figures will clarify and strengthen understanding.

Problem Solving Two interesting questions posed in the section labeled problem solving require reasoning rather than actual problem solving.

Connections The lesson connects prior learning by expressing congruence in terms of transformations. Transformations, congruence, and ordered pairs are connected through a question about location on a coordinate plane.

f.y.i.

- -

The approach to congruence of geometric shapes used in this lesson is called transformational geometry. Transformational geometry complements approaches using corresponding parts and coordinates and extends the range of problem-solving techniques. Analogous discussions of similarity focus on transforming size but not shape.

The teaching plan that follows shows how the suggestions for increasing the focus on the process standards can be implemented.

Revised Teaching Plan

Materials → Construction paper; grid paper; scissors

BEGIN THE LESSON by reviewing the definition of congruent figures as figures having the same size and shape. Engage students in a discussion of how congruent figures are identified by showing several pairs of figures—some clearly congruent, some obviously not, and some that look as though they might be—on the overhead. As you display each pair, ask students if the figures are congruent and why they think so. *When you are comparing figures for congruence, what is the first thing you look for? What helps you eliminate the possibility that two figures are congruent?* (Different shapes, different number or lengths of sides, obviously different sizes, and so on) *If you think two figures are congruent, what specifics do you check?* Try to elicit specific information from students to help them clarify their thinking. They might, for example, articulate that they begin by comparing general shape and size and then move to a closer examination of proportional relationships such as lengths of sides and measures of angles.

INTRODUCE ACTIVITIES WITH TRANSFORMATIONS by telling students that another way to explain congruence is to say that figures are congruent if they can be moved so that one exactly fits over the other; that is, they coincide. Show pairs of shapes on the overhead that are translations, reflections, rotations, and combinations of transformations. *Does the position or orientation of two figures affect their congruence?* (No.) *How does each of the transformations—a translation or slide; a rotation or turn; or a reflection or flip—affect a figure?* (These transformations change the position of the figure in the plane, but they do not change the size or shape of the figure.) Making this connection will help students understand why transformations can be used to define congruence.

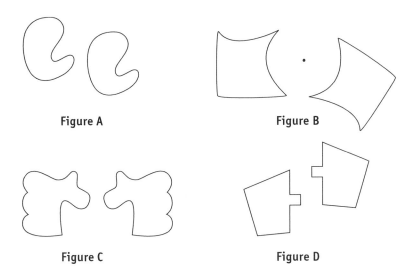

Figure A   Figure B

Figure C   Figure D

Four pairs of congruent shapes are shown. Figure A shows a translation, Figure B a rotation, Figure C a reflection, and Figure D a reflection combined with a translation.

Focus students' thinking on important properties of each transformation. *How do you determine if two figures are translation or slide images?* (The figures are the same but moved up or down; the distance between each point and its image is the same and in the same direction.) *When checking a rotation or turn, what relationships do you identify?* (Angle of rotation, center of rotation) *How do you identify a reflection or flip?* (Figures are mirror images; the figure is flipped over a line of symmetry.)

Ask students how they might prove that two figures in different positions are congruent. They should be able to explain they would find a sequence of transformations that would move one figure on to the other. *When more than one transformation has occurred, does it matter which is done first?* (No.) *How can we verify that?* Have students explain the transformations for pairs of figures displayed on the overhead. Doing this will help students understand that order of the transformations doesn't affect the congruence relationship and will reinforce visualization skills.

PAIR STUDENTS FOR A BRIEF exploration of congruence. Have each student cut one figure out of construction paper and copy the shape onto a piece of paper. Next to the original figure, students should draw a reflection and a rotation of the figure. Students should then exchange drawings along with the original shape for partners to check. Partners should be able to recreate the reflection and the rotation by manipulating the cutout and explain their thinking to each other. Drawing and checking these transformations will challenge students to think about the features and proportions of a shape and how, as the figure is transformed, those attributes must remain constant.

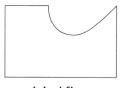

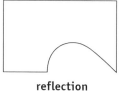

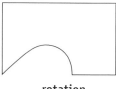

original figure   reflection   rotation

Judge the time required for this activity. If students understand the ideas readily, move on to the next activity. If you feel students need more time, introduce the next activity and consider having students complete it as homework.

HAVE STUDENTS DRAW x- and y-axis lines on grid paper. Instruct students to cut a shape from another piece of grid paper, making sure that the vertices of their shape fall on intersection points of the grid. They should then place their cutout shapes on the coordinate plane so that vertices can by easily identified with ordered pairs and outline the shapes. Tell students to record the ordered pairs. Students can then slide, reflect, and rotate the shape, identifying and recording each transformation and the ordered pairs for the vertices. Ask students to compare the ordered pairs for corresponding vertices and explain any relationships they can identify. For example, students may notice that sliding the figure 3 units to the right added 3 to each horizontal or x-coordinate. Have students describe another transformation of the same type, predict the vertices, and then check their prediction by carrying out the transformation. This activity will help students connect their thinking about geometric shapes to coordinate representations on a grid.

f.y.i.

When transformations are applied to symmetrical figures, it can be very difficult to identify what has occurred; the result of a rotation and a reflection might look the same. Encourage students to use irregular shapes to facilitate the identification process. If students use symmetrical figures, instruct them to label the vertices of their drawings to provide help in figuring out what transformations have taken place.

What Might Happen . . . What to Do

As they transform figures on the coordinate plane, students may have difficulty identifying corresponding vertices. Encourage students to label each vertex of the cutout with a letter of the alphabet. Demonstrate how to list the coordinates for each letter as a shape is transformed. This will help students keep track and will also make it easier to compare ordered pairs for each vertex.

CLOSE THE LESSON with a special challenge. Instruct students to create and present their own problems consisting of (a) coordinates for a pair of congruent figures related by a simple transformation and (b) incorrect coordinates for the image figure under the same transformation making the pair incongruent. Classmates can distinguish between the pairs of figures, explaining how they knew which pair was not congruent.

Student Pages

Students are now ready to complete exercises similar to those on the reduced student pages.

Assessment

By observing students as they worked through activities, you could assess their understanding of congruence and the properties of transformations. During the class discussions, students' responses provided another means of judging their knowledge of basic geometric concepts and coordinate graphing.

NCTM Standards Summary

In this reasoning-based lesson, students determined congruency between figures by comparing their attributes. Activities in which they represented and transformed geometric shapes enabled students to make predictions about and to explore the results of different combinations of translations. Examining representations of transformations of congruent figures on a coordinate grid gave students the opportunity to express geometric relationships using analytic methods and to add to their overall knowledge of these relationships. Discussions that required students to explain their thinking helped them to gain a much better understsanding of congruent figures and how transformations relate to congruence.

Standard 4 **Measurement**

AT THE EIGHTH GRADE LEVEL, measurement includes work with area and volume, ratios and rates, scale drawings, and angle relationships. Our lessons are derived from these important topics, and include a lesson that relates surface area and volume, a lesson on ratios and rates, a lesson on creating scale drawings, and a lesson that focuses on the classifications for one angle and the relationships for two angles.

Three lessons model how the process standards can be used to teach content. A fourth lesson is a hypothetical textbook lesson that we have revised to be more standards based. These four lessons do not represent the entire curriculum, but rather provide glimpses of how, with a more concentrated effort to incorporate the process standards, better mathematics teaching and learning can be achieved.

One lesson we have chosen relates surface area and volume. Through the process standards of representation, reasoning and proof, and connections, there are two main points established in this lesson. Students explore how the surface area changes as the volume is held constant and try to generalize about the figures that yield the greatest and least surface areas, and what effect multiplying the dimensions of a figure by a constant factor has on surface area and volume.

Another lesson we have chosen is one in which students explore ratios and rates. Through the process standards of problem solving and connections, students develop a better understanding of what a rate is, how to form one, and how to use rates to solve problems.

A third lesson that we have chosen is one in which students use scale drawings to enlarge or reduce a given figure. By incorporating the process standards of representation, reasoning and proof, and communication, students draw similar figures with grids and determine the scale used to create the similar figure.

The hypothetical textbook lesson that we have chosen to revise is a lesson in which students classify a single angle and the relationships between two angles. Through better incorporation of the process standards of problem solving, reasoning and proof, and communication, students are required to do more than memorize definitions. As they consider different combinations of applications of the angle relationships, students better understand the definitions and the differences between them.

Standard 4 Lessons

Relating Surface Area and Volume

Investigating Rates

Creating Scale Drawings

Exploring Angle Relationships

Relating Surface Area and Volume

Introduction

Objective → Students will compare geometric figures using measures of surface area and volume.

Context → Students are familiar with methods for finding surface area and volume and may have investigated relationships between perimeter and area. They have used ratios and solved problems involving scale drawings. Students will continue to analyze more complex geometric situations through the measurement process.

NCTM Standards Focus

In this lesson, students will use a hands-on approach to explore how surface area may change for a constant volume. The patterns in their results will help them make generalizations about figures with maximum and minimum surface areas, and they will express the relationships symbolically with formulas. As they study three-dimensional figures, students rely on their knowledge of ratio and scale to identify how multiplying dimensions by a constant factor affects surface area and volume, and they have the opportunity to combine several measurement skills.

Representation Students will use models to explore surface area. They will represent information by making geometric drawings and using algebraic symbolism to express relationships.

Reasoning and Proof Students will use reasoning to identify patterns in a table showing volumes and surface areas. They will predict the effect of multiplying dimensions on measures of surface area and volume and formulate an explanation of the relationship.

Connections Students will connect their understanding of surface area and volume to real-world situations involving cost minimization and temperature regulation. They will rely on prior knowledge about ratio, exponents, equations, and geometric figures to identify and explain relationships.

Teaching Plan

Materials → Student pages 100–101; linking cubes; wood, plastic, or sugar cubes

Preparation → Prior to the lesson, prepare models and/or drawings of figures described for display purposes.

INTRODUCE THE LESSON with a brief review of surface area and volume. Be sure all students understand that the volume of a three-dimensional figure is a measure of the amount of space it occupies, and that surface area is the total area of the figure's exterior surfaces.

Provide each student with a copy of student page 100. Form groups of 2–4 students and distribute at least 25 cubes to each group. Tell students that they will build some models to explore the relationship between surface area and volume. *Suppose you take 6 separate unit cubes, what is the total volume of those cubes?* (6 cubic units) *What is the total surface area? Explain.* (36 square units. For each cube S.A. = 6 × 1 square unit = 6 square units; 6 cubes would be 6 × 6 square units.)

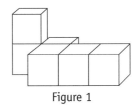

Figure 1

Arrange six cubes to match the figure shown in the margin.

- *If you were to put the six cubes together in a shape like this, would the volume still be 6 cubic units?* (Yes.)
- *What is the surface area of this figure? Find out by making the shape and counting the number of faces.* (24 square units)
- *Why is the surface area not 36 square units?* (Some of the sides have been covered up.)

Have the students experiment with different numbers of cubes. In each case they should try to find the shape with the least, or minimum, surface area and the shape with the greatest, or maximum, surface area. Explain that all cubes must share at least one face with at least one other cube—no loose cubes or cubes balanced on an edge are allowed. Instruct them to draw sketches and record their findings in the table on student page 100.

Allow 15–20 minutes for students to complete the activity and then have them use their data to discuss the results. Encourage students to observe patterns in their sketches and their tables.

- *Which shape always had the maximum surface area for a given number of cubes?* (The one that was a single row of cubes.)
- *If the number of unit cubes is* n, *what formula can be used to find the maximum surface area?* (S.A. = 4n + 2)
- *What is the maximum surface area of a shape made with 10 cubes?* (42 square units) *18 cubes?* (72 square units) *50 cubes?* (202 square units)

Now, focus students' attention on finding the minimum surface area. Have students refer to the data they recorded on student page 100.

- *What did you do to make the surface area as small as possible?* (Covered up or joined as many faces as possible)
- *When you used 8 cubes, what shape had the minimum surface area?* (A cube with 2 units on each edge)
- *What arrangement of 27 cubes would have the minimum surface area? Explain how you know.* (A 3 × 3 × 3 cube; a cubic shape gives the minimum surface area.)

CONTINUE THE EXPLORATION of surface area and volume. Since large quantities of cubes are needed to actually model the following situations, you may wish to collect cubes and appoint one group as model builders, another group to make drawings of the models, and a third group to compute answers using pencil and paper. Having a visual model available will reinforce students' understanding of how changes in linear dimensions affect measures of surface area and volume.

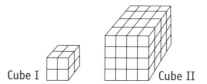

Cube I   Cube II

Display drawings or models of the two cubes shown. Explain that each edge of Cube I is 2 units. Each edge of Cube II is twice as long.

- *How does the surface area of Cube II compare to the surface area of Cube I?* (The surface area of Cube II is 96 square units, or 4 times the surface area of Cube I, which is 24 square units.)

- *How does the volume of Cube II compare to the volume of Cube I?* (The volume of Cube II is 64 cubic units, or 8 times the volume of Cube I, which is 8 cubic units.)

Point out that the ratio 1:2 is the scale factor for the edges of the cubes, and 1:4 is the scale factor for the area. *What is the scale factor for the volumes?* (1:8) Help students understand that when each linear dimension doubles, or increases by a factor of 2, the surface area grows by a factor of 4 because area is a square measure involving two dimensions; $2 \times 2 = 2^2 = 4$. Volume grows by a factor of 8 because volume is a cubic measure involving three dimensions; $2 \times 2 \times 2 = 2^3 = 8$. Ask students to predict what would happen if they tripled each edge of Cube I to create a Cube III, and tell them to justify their answer. (Surface area would be 9 times as great since $3 \times 3 = 3^2 = 9$; volume would be 27 times as great since $3 \times 3 \times 3 = 3^3 = 27$.)

Student Pages

Student page 100 provides recording space for the lesson activities involving maximum and minimum surface area. Student page 101 presents problems that allow students to apply their understanding of the lesson concepts.

Assessment

You observed students as they created models with a given volume and identified maximum and minimum surface area. During the discussion of the activity, it was possible to note students who were able to generalize their results both verbally and algebraically and apply the concepts to other situations. Students' responses and written work could be used to evaluate their proficiency computing surface areas and volumes and their insight into patterns of growth.

NCTM Standards Summary

Students created models to explore the relationship between a constant volume and surface area, and they represented the shapes they created with drawings. They used reasoning to identify patterns in their data and generalize their ideas verbally and symbolically. Throughout the lesson, students connected prior algebraic, numeric, geometric, and measurement knowledge to extend their understanding of surface area and volume. Opportunities for students to connect the principles they explored to a variety of real-world situations were provided on student pages.

Answers

Page 100

1. Maximums: 26, 30, 34, 38, 42;
   Minimums: 22, 24, 24, 29, 30
2. Maximum $S.A. = 4n + 2$
3. Surface areas: 6, 24, 54, 96, 384;
   Volume: 1, 8, 27, 64, 512
4. m^2; m^3
5. X: $V = 125,000$ in.^{3};
   Y: $V = 125,000$ in.^{3};
   Z: $V = 125,000$ in.^{3}
6. X: $S.A. = 15,000$ in.^{2};
   Y: $S.A. = 17,500$ in.^{2};
   Z: $S.A. = 19,500$ in.^{2}
7. X would be least expensive; it has the smallest surface area so it would require the least amount of metal.

Page 101

1. 9:49; 27:343
2. $S.A. = 9540$ m^2; $V = 84,240$ m^3
3. The animal stretches out to maximize surface area and gain as much heat as possible; it curls up to minimize surface area and conserve heat.
4. a. 3200 lbs.; b. 4 ft^2;
   c. 800 lbs/ft^2; pressure is doubled;
   d. pressure would triple to 1200 lbs/ft^2; e. *m*
5. No; the minimum surface area for a 10-cm cube with a volume of 1000 cm^3 is 600 cm^2.

Relating Surface Area and Volume

Answer the questions.

❶ Create two figures for each number of cubes indicated. Make one figure represent the maximum surface area for that number of cubes and the second figure represent the minimum surface area. Record your results in the table.

❷ Write a formula expressing the maximum surface area in terms of the number of cubes or volume of the figure. Use n to represent the number of cubes.

Number of Cubes	Maximum Surface Area (square units)	Minimum Surface Area (square units)
6		
7		
8		
9		
10		

Complete the table. Record the surface area and volume of each cube.

❸

Edge of Cube (units)	Surface Area (square units)	Volume (cubic units)
1		
2		
3		
4		
8		

❹ When the edge of a cube increases by a factor of m, the surface area increases by a factor of _____ and the volume increases by a factor of _____.

A designer has submitted plans for three metal storage boxes to a manufacturer.

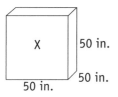

X — 50 in. / 50 in. / 50 in.

Y — 25 in. / 50 in. / 100 in.

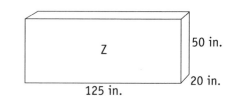

Z — 50 in. / 20 in. / 125 in.

❺ Find the volume for each box.   *X* _____   *Y* _____   *Z* _____

❻ Find the surface area of each box.   *X* _____   *Y* _____   *Z* _____

❼ If each box was constructed from the same metal, for which box would the cost of the metal be least expensive? Explain.

Standard 4 Measurement

Relating Surface Area and Volume

Answer the questions.

1 The ratio of the edges of two cubes is 3:7. What is the ratio of their surface areas? What is the ratio of their volumes?

2 A scale model of a new movie multiplex was built for display. The scale used was 5 cm = 3 m. The scale model required 26,500 square centimeters of cardboard for the exterior surfaces. What will the area of the exterior surface of the multiplex be?
The volume of the scale model is 390,000 cubic centimeters.
What will the volume of the multiplex be?

3 All animals gain or lose heat from the environment in proportion to their body surface area. The amount of heat that must be gained or lost is proportional to the animal's body volume. Explain why an animal would stretch out to bask in the sun and then curl up when it goes to sleep at night.

4 Suppose a 1-foot metal cube weighs 400 pounds. The bottom face supports the entire weight of the cube. The pressure exerted on the bottom face is equal to the weight of the cube divided by the area of the bottom face. In this case, the pressure is 400 pounds per square foot. Suppose another cube measuring
2 feet on each side is made of the same metal.
  a. What is the weight of the 2-foot cube?
  b. What is the area of the bottom face of the 2-foot cube?
  c. What is the pressure on the bottom face of the 2-foot cube? Compare this with the 1-foot cube.
  d. Predict what the pressure would be on the bottom face of a similar 3-foot cube. Verify your prediction.
  e. In general, if the side of the cube increases by a factor of m, by what factor will the pressure increase?

5 A cereal manufacturer wants a cardboard box with a volume of 1,000 cubic centimeters and a surface area of 560 square centimeters. Can the manufacturer achieve its goal? Explain.

Investigating Rates

Introduction

Objective → Students will solve problems involving rates.

Context → Students have used units of measure to describe length, volume and capacity, and time. In this lesson they apply their knowledge of measurement as they solve rate problems. They will continue to work with rates involving various units of measure and will use algorithms for calculating rates and solving rate problems.

NCTM Standards Focus

Traditionally, students have been given the algorithm for solving rate problems. In this standards-based lesson they apply their intuitive understanding of rate to the solution of rate problems. Students formulate their own strategies for solving rate problems.

Problem Solving Students analyze problems to identify the information needed to solve them. They devise strategies to solve the problems.

Connections Students use division and other operations to calculate and work with rates. They work with various units of measure and relate them to each other in new ways.

Teaching Plan

Materials → Student pages 106–107; calculators

BEGIN THE LESSON with a quick activity to help students focus on units of measure. Ask them to name all the units of measure they can think of. Make a list of these units. As the list grows, ask for ways to organize the items. Students will probably suggest grouping units according to what is measured: for example, distance or length, weight, capacity.

Tell students they are going to be solving problems in which they use rates. Ask for various examples of rates, such as miles per hour or dollars per hour. Place students in groups of two to four and ask them to do the first problem on student page 106. If students are having trouble getting started, ask them what information they have about each trip that is similar. *How might you measure how fast things travel?*

If some students are still having trouble, suggest that they simplify the numbers to help them see the relationship between miles and hours. *Suppose you traveled 30 miles in 1 hour. How fast were you going?* (30 miles per hour) *Now suppose you traveled 30 miles over an unpaved road, and it took you 2 hours to go that far. You could say you went at a speed of 30 miles per 2 hours. Usually speed is given in miles per hour, not per 2 hours. How many miles did you go in 1 hour? What was your speed in miles per hour?* (15 miles per hour) *What did you do to figure that out?* (divided miles by hours)

When groups are finished with the first problem, ask them to present their methods of solution. As they present their methods encourage other groups to ask questions. Make sure you ask these questions. *Could you have used something other than miles per hour as a unit of comparison? For example, could you have used miles per day?* (Here students need to realize that they could use a different unit for comparison if they can calculate the same unit for each trip. In the example of miles per day, they would need to be clear on what constituted a day—8 hours, 24 hours, or another amount, and then calculate the unit.)

If time permits ask students to use the information they have and solve the problem using a different unit of measure. It is important that students understand that in solving this problem they are not looking for a particular numerical answer; rather, they are trying to find common ground to compare two situations that on the surface look difficult to compare.

Ask students to summarize the solution. Melissa drove faster during Trip B. On Trip B, she drove 1,326 miles in 25.5 hours—an average speed of 52 miles per hour; on Trip A she drove 2,169 miles in 45 hours—an average speed of 48.2 miles per hour.

Have students look at the second problem. This problem should present more of a challenge to them. Not only will they need to determine how much coverage they get from a gallon of paint, they will also have to determine cost and which paint they will use. They will be asked to make a decision using mathematics as a tool. The decision involves not just finding out how much it costs to paint the wall, but also looking at other factors such as time versus cost. Make sure students look at this problem as if they actually had to do the painting.

If students have difficulty getting started, consider trying the following technique which focuses on communication. Have students describe what the problem asks them to do and how they might go about doing it, but do not let them use any numbers in their conversation. Students often rush towards solving a problem by pulling out numbers and performing some operations on them without getting a good picture of what is going on. This technique of describing the problem without the mention of any numbers may help students focus on what is happening. For example, in this problem students should be able to say that they need to decide which brand of paint is the better choice for painting a living room. They need to find the surface area of the walls which will require finding the area for each wall and subtracting the non-wall areas (700 ft² − 160 ft²). They will also need to determine how much a gallon (or some other unit they can work with) of each paint will cover and how much of each paint will be needed. Finally, they will need to figure the cost of each job and also consider other factors such as time spent painting with each brand.

When students have finished the problem, discuss their strategies and solutions. Make sure students understand that while they can choose either Brand A or Brand B, they must have a reason they can back up with facts.

Methods Students Might Use

- Brand A covers 360 square feet per gallon ($\frac{900}{2.5}$). One and a half gallons could theoretically paint the surface, but this leaves no room for error, nor would you have any paint left over for touch ups later on. One gallon and three quarts is safer for this brand. This would cost $95. Another option would be to get two gallons for $100 and have more paint left over. Either choice is reasonable.

- Brand B covers 429 square feet per gallon ($\frac{1500}{3.5}$). With Brand B you need to cover twice the area since you are using two coats; you have 1080 square feet to cover. This could be done with 2 gallons and 3 quarts (1179 square feet), with a little paint left for touch up. Buying either 3 gallons ($90) or 2 gallons and 3 quarts ($84) would be a reasonable choice.

- If money is the only object, it makes sense to choose Brand B because it costs less ($95 − $84 = $11). The big question is whether the time needed to put on a second coat of paint is worth $11 dollars. If the time required is worth more to you than $11 dollars, you should choose Brand A.

Review page 107 with students. They may have seen offers similar to these in advertisements. It is important for students to recognize the need to analyze these kinds of ads with the tools of mathematics and use their problem-solving skills to make intelligent decisions based on their analysis.

Student Pages

Student page 106 presents two rate problems that students solve during the lesson. Student page 107 contains problems that involve finding rates and using that information in decision making.

Assessment

As students worked together to solve the problems, you could note the strategies they used to find rates. The way they discussed the given information and the result they wanted helped you see whether they understood the concept of rate. Their ability to use division to find rates gave you more information about their understanding of the meaning of *per* in a rate and the basic ideas of the lesson.

NCTM Standards Summary

Students solved problems by deriving rates based on given units of measurement. They identified the information they needed and devised strategies to solve the problems. They shared their strategies with each other. They also made mathematical connections between various units of measure and used division appropriately.

Answers

Page 106
See lesson for solutions.

Page 107
1. The Old Fashioned Phone Company
2. 10-10-1010: 8.1¢ per min; Old Fashioned: 8.09¢ per min
3–4. Answers will vary; students should offer logical reasons.
5. Get-12-Free: $185.84; Two-for-One: $219.80
6. Get-12-Free: about $9.29; Two-for-One: $10.99
7. Get-12-Free
8. Answers may vary.

Investigating Rates

Solve the problems.

① Melissa kept logs of trips she took. Here are the records for each trip. During which trip did she drive faster?

Trip A	
Day 1	385 miles in $7\frac{1}{2}$ hours.
Day 2	476 miles in 10 hours
Day 3	442 miles in $9\frac{1}{2}$ hours
Day 4	536 miles in $11\frac{1}{4}$ hours
Day 5	330 miles in $6\frac{3}{4}$ hours

Trip B	
Day 1	370 miles in $7\frac{1}{2}$ hours
Day 2	485 miles in $9\frac{1}{4}$ hours
Day 3	245 miles in $4\frac{1}{2}$ hours
Day 4	226 miles in $4\frac{1}{4}$ hours

② Jasmine wants to paint her living room. She has four walls to paint. Two of the walls are 19 ft by 10 ft and the other two are 16 ft by 10 ft. There are two open entries into the living room in the walls. One is 8 ft by 10 ft and the other is 4 ft by 10 ft. There is a picture window that is 4 ft by 10 ft. She has two choices for paint. Both are comparable in quality. How much will it cost to do the paint job using each brand of paint? Which brand would you choose and why?

- Brand A can cover a surface in one coat and costs $50 per gallon and $15 per quart. A friend said they used $2\frac{1}{2}$ gallons of this paint for one coat covering 900 square feet.

- Brand B needs two coats and costs $30 per gallon and $8 per quart. Another friend told you they used $3\frac{1}{2}$ gallons of this paint to cover 1500 square feet with one coat.

Standard 4 Measurement

Investigating Rates

Solve the problems.

Use the following information to answer questions 1–4.

- The 10-10-1010 Telephone Company advertises that you can talk for up to 20 minutes for only 99¢. Each additional minute costs 5¢. You also must pay a monthly service charge of $5.50.

- The Old Fashioned Phone Company charges 7¢ per minute plus a monthly service charge of $5.50.

Calls that Family A made this month	
5	five minute calls
10	ten minute calls
7	fifteen minute calls
10	twenty minute calls
3	twenty-five minute calls

1 Which phone company would charge the least this month?

2 What would the family's actual per minute rate be for each phone company?

3 Which company would you pick for your phone service? Why?

4 Why might another family pick a different phone company?

Use the following information to answer questions 5–9.

- The Get-12-Free Music Club offers new members 12 free CDs when they join the club. They must also buy 4 CDs at the regular club price of $16.98. A $2.50 shipping and handling fee will be charged for each CD received (this applies to free CDs).

- The Two-for-One Music Club offers new members 2 CDs for the price of one. Whenever a member orders a CD, he or she can pick another one for free. Each CD costs $16.98 and there is a shipping charge of $2.50 per CD (including the free ones).

5 If someone joins each club and gets 20 CDs the first year, how much will he or she pay?

6 What is the average cost of a CD through each club?

7 Which club gives the best deal?

8 Which club would you join if you were going to join a club? Why?

Creating Scale Drawings

Introduction

Objective → Students will draw similar figures with grids and determine ratios between the figures.

Context → Students have used ratio and proportion to describe number relationships and have used similarity to describe geometric shapes. They will go on to learn about trigonometric ratios and solve indirect measurement problems.

NCTM Standards Focus

In this lesson, students will explore methods for enlarging or reducing a given figure. They will examine their drawings and identify the proportional relationship between the different representations. Using the hands-on approach in the lesson, students will develop a more intuitive understanding of the concepts of similarity and scale.

Representation Students will represent concrete models using geometric drawings. They will represent the relationships between different drawings using a ratio or scale.

Reasoning and Proof Students will develop their own methods of changing the size of a given figure. They will justify the accuracy of their methods using formal mathematical definitions of similarity. Students will reason abstractly to identify the scale relationship between different representations and interpret the meaning of a scale factor.

Communication Students will discuss how to determine similarity and scale factors. They will discuss their methods for enlarging and reducing drawings and will help each other interpret information from scale drawings.

Teaching Plan

Materials → Student pages 112–113; selected pattern blocks (hexagon, trapezoid, and triangle—one set per group); metric and standard rulers, protractors (optional)

BEGIN THE LESSON with a brief discussion of the concept of similarity by having students explain when two figures are similar. Students should explain that similar figures have the same shape but are not necessarily the same size, that their corresponding angles are congruent, and that the ratios of corresponding sides are equal. Encourage students to give some examples of similarity from real-world situations. Typical examples include maps, blueprints, and enlargements or reductions of photographs.

Invite students to consider what happens when a photograph is enlarged to create a similar photo. *If the length of an enlarged photograph is twice the length of the original, how does the width of the enlarged photo compare to the original?* (It is twice the width of the original.) *If the length of a slanted line segment between two points on the original photo is 2 inches, what will this slanted line segment measure on the enlargement?* (4 inches)

DISTRIBUTE STUDENT PAGE 112. Students will use the grids on this page to make drawings and enlargements of pattern blocks. It may be helpful to provide several copies of student page 112 for each student so that they can experiment with different strategies and refine their drawings. Divide students into groups of 3 or 4, and provide each group with a set of three pattern blocks. Display the three pattern block shapes and discuss the attributes of each. Ask students to consider how they could use the grids on the student page to draw the shapes and then make enlarged drawings of those shapes. Tell students that they should discuss their strategies, but that each student is to make his/her own drawing. Encourage students to share their methods.

Methods Students Might Use

- Students might trace the shape onto the centimeter grid, then transfer the lines square-by-square onto the inch grid to create an enlarged shape. This results in approximately a 1:2.5 ratio.

- They might trace the shape onto either grid, then create a larger similar version on the same grid, covering two squares where the original drawing covered one square. This results in a 1:2 ratio.

No matter which method students use, suggest the following steps to help them create a more accurate reproduction:

- Copy the original shapes onto a grid.
- Note where the lines of the drawing intersect grid lines.
- Mark the corresponding intersection points onto the larger grid.
- Connect the marks to create the enlarged drawing

Encourage students to discuss their drawings. *What is the difference between the original and new shape?* (The lengths of the corresponding sides of the new shape are greater.) *What remains the same?* If students say, "the shapes are the same," ask them to be more specific. *What feature of the shapes does not change?* (The angles; the corresponding angles are congruent.) *How could you prove that your drawings are similar, that is, that even though their sides are not the same length, their angles are congruent?* Students should suggest measuring the corresponding angles to prove that they are congruent, and measuring the lengths of corresponding sides to make sure the ratio for each pair of sides is equal. You might wish to have them verify this by using rulers and protractors to check measurements.

f.y.i.

You might wish to ask if any students have ever heard of a device called a *pantograph*. Explain that a pantograph is a framework of jointed rods that can be adjusted to reproduce a drawing on the same or different scale. The user traces a drawing, which is copied.

f.y.i.

Angle measurement is the key to similarity. Similar figures have congruent angles. The sides of the figures may be increased or decreased, but that change must occur proportionally so as not to affect the size of the angles.

DIRECT STUDENT'S ATTENTION to the corresponding sides of similar figures. Challenge students to find the scale factor that expresses the difference in the lengths of the sides of between the smaller and larger drawings. *What measurements need to be taken to make comparisons between lengths of corresponding sides?* If students transferred their drawings square-by-square from the centimeter grid to the inch grid, one way to express the scale would be 1 cm = 1 in. However, in order for the scale factor to be meaningful, both measures should be expressed in the same units. Students can use a metric ruler to determine the number of centimeters in an inch, or they can measure the length of corresponding sides on both grids in centimeters. If, for example, a side that was 2 cm now corresponds to a side of 2 inches, and 2 inches = 5.08 cm (students may use approximations such as 5 cm or 5.1 cm) then 1 inch = 2.54 cm. It follows that the new drawing is 2.54 (or about 2.5) times the size of the original drawing.

If students enlarged their figure on the same grid, perhaps using two squares for each one, then the ratio is simply 1:2 and the new drawing is twice the size of the original. Note that in both cases the scale factor relates to linear dimensions only. Point out that the expression "twice as large" can be interpreted differently depending on context—"twice as large" would not correctly compare areas here.

CONCLUDE THE LESSON by having students consider how to make a smaller drawing of the one shown on student page 113. Have students discuss the differences involved in completing this drawing as opposed to making a geometric shape, and encourage them to brainstorm ways they can adapt the process they used in the first part of the lesson. One possible method would be for students to draw or place a centimeter grid over the picture, then reduce it by transferring a line covering two squares to one square. Alternatively, they could draw an inch grid over the picture and transfer it to the smaller centimeter grid.

Instruct students to summarize the methods they use to create their drawings and to express the proportional relationship between their original and reduced versions. Also, have students explain any methods they tried that did not seem to work well and give reasons why they think this was so. Students who can analyze their work in this way will demonstrate their understanding of concepts involving measurement and ratio.

Student Pages

Student page 112 contains the centimeter and inch grids to be used for the first lesson activity. Student page 113 presents a simple line drawing to be drawn in a reduced version on the $\frac{1}{4}$-inch grid below it. If time permits, use this page as a second in-class activity. You might prefer to assign the page as homework and follow up with an in-class discussion.

Assessment

During the introductory discussion, it was possible to assess students' understanding of the concept of similarity. As students worked on the pattern-block activity, it was possible to observe the strategies they used to create an enlarged drawing. Judging their fluency with ratio and proportion could be accomplished as students described the relationship between the sizes of their two drawings. Finally, it was possible to determine student's flexibility of thinking as they approached the problem of reducing a given picture and judged the accuracy of their final product.

NCTM Standards Summary

As students represented concrete models and drawings with versions that were scaled up or scaled down, they used their own understandings to devise methods for changing the size of a drawing and justified the accuracy of their work by relying on the mathematical definition of similarity. Students also interpreted relationships represented by different grids and measurements to express comparisons between drawings in terms of ratios and scale factors. Throughout the lesson, students explained and compared their methods and results and developed new insights by doing so. Sharing of ideas reinforced the fact that there are usually alternative approaches to a problem. Since the challenges presented in the lesson allowed for individual variation, students had the opportunity to identify an approach that suited their thinking.

Answers

Pages 112–113
Check students' completed drawings.

Creating Scale Drawings

Use the grids below to make an enlarged drawing of a geometric shape.

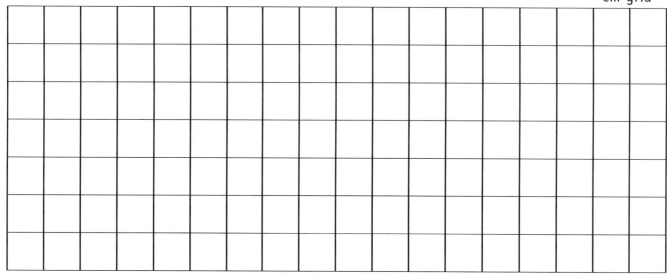

cm grid

inch grid

Standard 4 Measurement

Creating Scale Drawings

Make a reduced drawing of the picture in the box. Explain the relationship between the size of the two drawings and express the relationship as a ratio. Show your work.

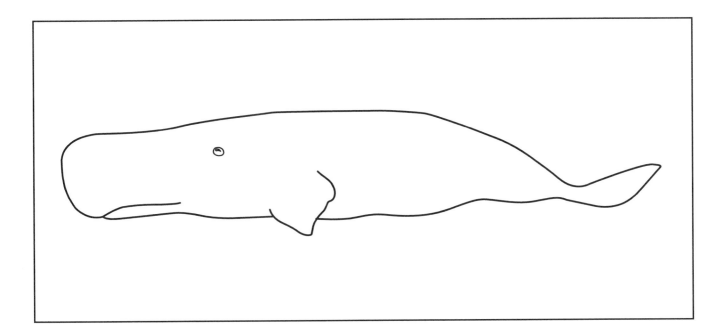

$\frac{1}{4}$-inch grid

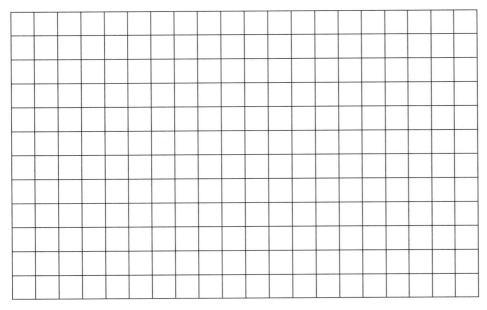

Exploring Angle Relationships

Introduction

Objective → Students will measure and classify acute, right, obtuse, and straight angles and will identify pairs of angles as adjacent, complementary, supplementary, vertical, and congruent.

Context → This lesson appears early in a geometry unit. Students have identified planes, points on the plane, lines, and angles. They will continue the study of angle relationships in parallel lines and work on constructions.

Exploring Angle Relationships
. . . .

Learn

Look around your school building and your home. There are angles everywhere.

These angles have special names.

- An **acute angle** is an angle that measures between 0° and 90°

- A **right angle** is an angle that measures 90°, and is formed by two perpendicular rays.

- An **obtuse angle** is an angle that measures between 90° and 180° degrees.

- A **straight angle** is an angle that measures 180°.

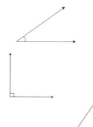

Pairs of angles can be related in different ways.

Two angles that have the same measure are called **congruent angles**.

These angles are formed by intersecting lines. The angles opposite each other have equal measures. They are called **vertical angles.**

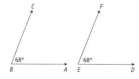

Discuss

Can you draw a figure that has at least one acute angle, one right angle, and one obtuse angle? Explain why or why not.

NCTM Process Standards Analysis and Focus

The standards analysis examines how the process standards have been incorporated into the above lesson. By increasing the focus on three of the process standards, a more effective and meaningful lesson can be presented. The suggestions offered can help you to think about how this might be accomplished.

Problem Solving Identifying and classifying angles according to their definitions is the focus of this lesson. Problem solving is not involved.

Suggestion → Encourage student involvement by asking students to draw angles and determine relationships between the pairs of angles drawn. Creating angles with required attributes will help students understand the

• •

Angles that have a common vertex and a common side between them are called **adjacent angles.**

Two angles whose sum measures 90° are called **complementary angles.**

Two angles whose sum measures 180° are called **supplementary angles**.

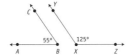

Try

Draw an example of each.

1. An acute angle

2. A right angle

3. An obtuse angle

4. A straight angle

5. Two congruent angles

6. A pair of vertical angles

7. Two adjacent angles

8. Two complementary angles

9. Two supplementary angles

10. An obtuse angle and an acute angle that are adjacent angles

Practice

Find the measure of each angle.

11. ∠QZN

12. ∠MZX

13. ∠PZN

14. ∠PXA

15. ∠AXQ

16. ∠QXB

17. ∠ANZ

18. ∠MNB

19. ∠MZP

20. ∠QXN

21. ∠ZXN

22. ∠MZP

23. Which pairs of angles are vertical angles?

24. Which pairs of angles are complementary? supplementary? congruent?

distinctions between those angles and the definitions introduced in the lesson.

Reasoning and Proof The lesson presents drawings and asks students to figure out missing angle measures in the drawings by applying definitions. Questions that require students to use reasoning and demonstrate their understanding are not posed until the end of the lesson.

Suggestion → Ask students to explain why their drawings meet given requirements. Doing so will reinforce their understanding of angles and angle relationships. Having students consider whether angle pairs can belong to more than one category, such as being both vertical and complementary, will add insight into the definitions.

Communication Students discuss angle relationships in triangles.

Written work involves identifying angles and figuring out measures.

Suggestion → Prompt students to incorporate terms and definitions as they explain their thinking and their problem-solving methods. As students describe their methods for finding missing measures, they will clarify these processes and show that the same result may often be reached by different methods.

Connections Opportunities for identifying angles in the real world are limited.

Representation The lesson uses geometric drawings to present ideas or information.

The teaching plan that follows shows how the suggestions for increasing the focus on the process standards can be implemented.

Revised Teaching Plan

BEGIN THE LESSON by reviewing acute, obtuse, right, straight, complementary, and supplementary angles with the class. Discuss the usefulness of classifying different types of angles and angle relationships, explaining that in the real world, these general descriptions allow people to communicate information efficiently. An understanding of angle relationships also enhances one's ability to execute and appreciate design.

INVITE STUDENTS TO FIND EXAMPLES of the different types of angles in the classroom. Have students explain the thinking that helps them classify these angles. Encourage them to use right angles and straight angles as benchmarks. For example, if asked how they might recognize an acute angle, students might explain that since the angle is smaller than a corner or right angle, it is acute. Such discussion will help students develop their intuition about angle relationships. Be sure to point out that when angles are very close to these benchmarks, they may be difficult to identify and actual measurement may be required.

Have students draw, label, and identify specific angles to represent each of the general types discussed. Encourage students to approach this activity in two ways: by drawing angles that are separate from one another, and by drawing a straight line and then subdividing with rays extending from a common vertex. Explain that in the first instance, students may or may not use three letters to label angles, but in the second instance, they must use this labeling convention. Creating different representations of angles will reinforce students' understanding of the definitions and will help them recognize angles in problem-solving situations in which drawings are likely to be more complicated.

f.y.i.

Frequently things are named because they fit a known definition. An interesting point for students to consider is the connection between the attributes of acute and obtuse angles and the ordinary English meaning of those words.

f.y.i.

Depending on the time available, you might consider having students divide a line into angles and then identify the angles created. This could be part of a homework assignment.

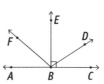

Acute angle ∠ABF, ∠FBE, ∠EBD, ∠DBC
Right angle ∠ABE, ∠EBC
Obtuse angle ∠ABD, ∠FBD, ∠FBC
Straight angle ∠ABC
Complementary angles ∠ABF and ∠FBE, ∠EBD and ∠DBC
Supplementary angles ∠ABD and ∠DBC

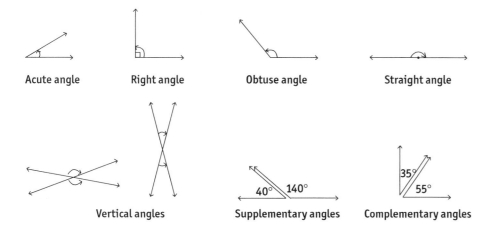

Acute angle   Right angle   Obtuse angle   Straight angle

Vertical angles   Supplementary angles   Complementary angles

f.y.i.

Shading pairs of angles with colored chalk visually highlights the angles being described and the relationships that exist between them. Color cues may be helpful to students who have difficulty listening to and following the alphabetical naming conventions used to indicate the angles.

Allow time for students to share their drawings and discuss the complementary and supplementary angle relationships that exist in their drawings. To clarify and reinforce understanding, draw and label additional angles on the board and ask students to define and identify relationships that can be found in the drawings.

What Might Happen . . . What to Do

Students often do not understand that pairs of complementary and supplementary angles may be, but do not have to be, adjacent. Be sure to give examples of both formats.

POSE QUESTIONS TO HELP STUDENTS make important distinctions among angle relationships. *Can a pair of vertical angles be complementary? Supplementary? Explain.* (Yes, both can measure 45° or both can measure 90°.) *Is the supplement of an obtuse angle always an acute angle?* (Yes.) *Why?* (Since an obtuse angle measures more than 90°, its supplement must measure less than 90°.) *Can the complement of an acute angle ever be a right angle?* (No.) *Why?* (Since the sum must measure 90°, one angle cannot be a right angle, which always has a measure of 90°.) This type of discussion prompts students to reason about angle relationships and thus broaden their understanding.

Encourage students to explore angle relationships by having them draw and label their own representations of angle combinations such as vertical obtuse angles or complementary adjacent angles. Ask students to identify all angle relationships and types of angles they have shown and to summarize the information by including brief definitions in their own words. Students can partner to critique each other's work. The reasoning and communication involved in this activity will strengthen students' understanding of the concepts.

Reproduce the following drawing on the board or on an overhead transparency, and use it to develop an understanding of how to find missing angle measures. Provide an opportunity for students to explain the reasoning used to find each angle measure.

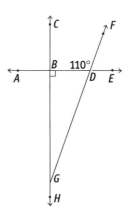

Identify all the right angles in the drawing and explain how you know. Find the measure of ∠BDG and explain your reasoning. (The measure can be found by identifying ∠BDG as supplementary to the given ∠BDF or by identifying ∠FDE as supplementary to ∠BDF and then using vertical angles.) *What is the measure of ∠BGD? Explain.* (20°; The three angles of △BGD equal 180°, and since ∠B of the triangle is 90° and ∠D is 70°, ∠G must be 20°.) As students explain their reasoning and listen to others, they will recognize that there are often several ways to solve a problem. Having students find all the missing angle measures and identify types of angles and angle relationships in the drawing will reinforce their understanding of all the lesson concepts. Students might also check that the measures they find for the angles in △BDG add to 180°.

Extension

Have students solve the following problem in any way they choose.
The complement of an angle measures five times the angle. Find the measure of each angle. (15°, 75°)

Student Pages

Students should now be ready to complete exercises similar to those on the reduced student pages.

Assessment

As students made and explained their drawings, there were opportunities to assess their understanding of angle names and relationships between angles. Students' abilities to apply basic angle concepts in problem-solving situations could be evaluated as they answered questions and participated in discussions.

NCTM Standards Summary

Involving students in drawing activities required them to reason about the attributes that characterize different angles and pairs of angles. Creating representations of various angle relationships and presenting justifications for their drawings developed and reinforced students' understanding of definitions and relationships. Discussing methods for finding missing angle measures gave students an opportunity to listen to approaches that might be different from their own. In this way, students both reviewed the meaning of terms and were able to recognize firsthand that there is often more than one way to arrive at an answer. Integrating questions that involved critical thinking into the teaching of the lesson—rather than at the end of the exercises—enhanced communication and helped students to make important distinctions among the definitions, allowing for any misconceptions to be promptly clarified.

Standard 5 **Data Analysis and Probability**

AT THE EIGHTH GRADE LEVEL, data analysis and probability includes a lot of work with different graphical representations of data, and probability concepts. Our lessons are derived from these important topics, and include a lesson on calculating the probability of dependent and independent events, a lesson in which students explore how graphs can be used to misrepresent data, a lesson on using scatter plots to represent data, and a lesson on box-and-whisker plots.

Three lessons model how the process standards can be used to teach content. A fourth lesson is a hypothetical textbook lesson that we have revised to be more standards based. These four lessons do not represent the entire curriculum, but rather provide glimpses of how, with a more concentrated effort to incorporate the process standards, better mathematics teaching and learning can be achieved.

In one lesson we have chosen, students calculate the probability of dependent and independent events. Using the process standards of representation and connections, students use manipulatives to model real-world situations of dependent and independent events.

Another lesson we have chosen is one that focuses students on ways in which representations of data can be misleading to the reader. Applying the process standards of representation, communication, and problem solving, students study two different graphs that represent the same data. They see how perceptions can be manipulated so that readers come away with a favorable impression of not-so-favorable data.

A third lesson that we have chosen is one in which students make and interpret scatter plots. Using the process standards of representation, communication, and connections, students analyze scatter plots to identify a relationship between two sets of data. Students draw and analyze a line of best fit for the data.

The hypothetical textbook lesson that we have chosen to revise is a lesson in which students make and interpret box-and-whisker plots. Through better incorporation of the process standards of representation, reasoning and proof, and communication, students are provided a more in-depth discussion of these representations, finding out more about how they are made, and what information is conveyed in a box-and-whisker plot.

Standard 5 Lessons

Calculating Probability

**Representing Data in
Different Ways**

Modeling Data with Scatterplots

**Interpreting and Making
Box-and-Whisker Plots**

Calculating Probability

Introduction

Objective → Students will calculate the probability in composite situations involving both *independent* and *dependent* events.

Context → Students have had experience with simple probability exercises in earlier grades. They have learned about theoretical and experimental probabilities and have used tree diagrams to calculate simple probabilities.

NCTM Standards Focus

In this lesson, students extend their understanding beyond finding simple probability. They create and examine tree diagrams and lists of possible outcomes to distinguish between probabilities for composite events that involve both independent and dependent situations, and they use multiplication to solve probability problems.

Representation Students represent possible outcomes of events visually using tree diagrams. They distinguish among different situations in order to apply correct solution methods.

Communication Students explain the various methods they use to determine possible outcomes. They communicate their understanding both orally and in writing.

Connections Students connect tree diagrams and tables representing outcomes to the use of multiplication to determine the probability of an event. They use tree diagrams to understand the difference between independent and dependent events.

Teaching Plan

Materials → Student pages 126–127; calculators; overhead projector (optional)

BEGIN BY TELLING STUDENTS that in this lesson they will work with probability problems that represent both independent and dependent events. Ask students to define the word *independent*. They should suggest that something that "stands on its own" is independent. Explain that in probability, independent events are those that are not effected by other events. Then ask students to define the word *dependent*. Students should understand that dependent is the opposite of independent, that when something is dependent, it relies on something other than itself. In probability, a dependent event is one that is effected by another event that happens before it.

Briefly review the definition of probability as the number of favorable outcomes compared to the number of possible outcomes. Remind students how to determine and state the probability of a simple event by showing a six-sided number cube and asking them to give the probability of getting a

3 in a single toss. Review that there are 6 possible outcomes, only one of which is a 3, making the probability 1 out of 6, or $\frac{1}{6}$. Pose a few similar questions.

Discuss that tossing a fair number cube represents a single independent event; only one occurrence is involved and nothing other than chance effects the outcome. Selecting a single card at random from a deck or randomly picking a particular color counter from a bag are additional examples of single independent events.

DISTRIBUTE STUDENT PAGE 126. Call attention to the first question in which a fair number cube and a coin are tossed. Have students consider the difference between this problem and tossing a single number cube. Establish that tossing a coin and rolling a number cube are independent events; the outcome for each is independent of the other. In this case, however, rather than the probability resulting from a single occurrence, the outcome includes two things happening, and is considered *composite*. This problem represents probability for composite independent events.

Allow students several minutes to find the possible outcomes for this problem and list them on their worksheets. Ask students to share their results and their methods. If making lists, outcome grids, and tree diagrams are not all represented, be sure to go over each of these methods to provide alternate approaches for finding outcomes. Give special attention to the tree diagram method as it will be used later in the lesson. Students should find twelve possible outcomes, six for heads combined with numbers 1–6; and six for tails combined with numbers 1–6.

Next, instruct students to refer to their list of outcomes from the first question to answer the second question on the worksheet in which they find the probability of getting heads and an even number. Use this second question and answer to initiate a review of using multiplication to determine specific outcomes. Students should see from their list of outcomes that the probability for heads is $\frac{1}{2}$ since heads comes up half of the time. Half of the outcomes with heads have even numbers. $\frac{1}{2}$ of $\frac{1}{2} = \frac{1}{2} \times \frac{1}{2} = \frac{1}{4}$.

Now ask students to complete the third question in which they find the probability for tails and a number less than 5. Discuss their solutions and encourage students to use multiplication to solve the problem. Students should explain that the probability for tails is $\frac{1}{2}$ and the probability for a number less than 5 is 4 out of 6, or $\frac{2}{3}$. ($\frac{1}{2} \times \frac{2}{3} = \frac{2}{6}$ or $\frac{1}{3}$) You may choose to have students complete the last problem in class or assign it for homework.

Provide problems for students to solve to affirm their understanding.

- A number cube is tossed three times. What is the probability that you will get a number less than 3 on the first toss, an even number on the second toss, and a 4 on the third toss? ($\frac{1}{36}$; $\frac{1}{3} \times \frac{1}{2} \times \frac{1}{6}$)

- A card is selected at random from a fair deck, placed back into the deck, and then a second card is selected. What is the probability that the first card will be red and the second card will be a black 4? ($\frac{1}{52}$; $\frac{1}{2} \times \frac{1}{26}$)

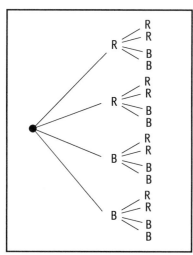

With Replacement

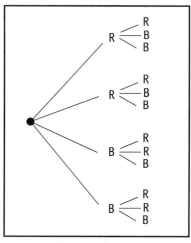

Without Replacement

NOW INTRODUCE STUDENTS TO determining possible outcomes for dependent events. The method suggested here will provide a visual connection to help students distinguish between dependent and independent events. Ask students to draw a tree diagram and to list the possible outcomes for a situation in which a marble is picked from a bag containing 2 red and 2 blue marbles, placed back into the bag, and then a second marble is picked. When they have completed their diagrams and lists, ask them to find the probability that both marbles are red. Place a diagram on the board or overhead and reinforce that there are 4 favorable out of 16 possible outcomes for picking 2 red marbles when the marble is replaced after the first pick. The probability of picking 2 red marbles *with replacement* is $\frac{1}{4}$.

Next, have students make a tree diagram and list possible outcomes representing 2 picks from the same bag, but this time, *not* replacing the marble after the first pick. Again, ask students to identify the probability for picking 2 red marbles. Place the diagram on the board or overhead. Students should see that because the marble was not replaced, instead of 16 possible outcomes, there are only 12 possible outcomes, two of which are favorable for both marbles being red. Emphasize that not replacing the marble reduced the number of marbles available for the second pick. The probability for picking 2 red marbles *without replacement* is $\frac{2}{12}$ or $\frac{1}{6}$.

Explain that finding the probability *with replacement* represents another example of *independent events,* since the situation is the same at the start of each pick. However, *without replacement,* the situation is different. This is an example of a *dependent event*; the outcome of the second event is effected by the first event.

Now have students use multiplication to find the probability of each event. For getting 2 red marbles with replacement, their sentence should be $\frac{1}{4} \times \frac{1}{4} = \frac{1}{16}$. This is like other problems students have solved.

Explain that for getting 2 red marbles without replacement, we assume that the first event we were looking for, in this case picking a red, occurred because that's the situation we are interested in. Assuming a red marble was removed, there will be only 3 marbles left and only one of the three will be red. The sentence for 2 red marbles without replacement should be $\frac{1}{4} \times \frac{1}{3} = \frac{1}{12}$.

Pose another problem.

> Two names are picked from a hat to determine who will have clean-up duty. Today, Jean, Jane, Jay, John, and Jerry have their names in the hat. What is the probability that both Jane and Jerry will have their names picked?
> ($\frac{1}{5} \times \frac{1}{4} = \frac{1}{20}$)

To conclude the lesson, distribute student page 127 and have students answer the questions presented.

Student Pages

Student page 126 provides recording space for lesson activities. Student page 127 offers additional practice problems.

Assessment

As students made diagrams and tables and explained their methods you could assess their ability to identify possible outcomes. Their answers and explanations helped you evaluate their understanding of how to determine the probability of specific outcomes. Student pages offer opportunities for assessment of individual skills.

NCTM Summary

In this lesson, students represented possible outcomes in a variety of ways. They connected multiplication with those representations, allowing them to understand how multiplication is used to determine outcomes. They examined problems representing different types of probability problems and distinguished among them. As students explained their solutions and their methods, students offered additional ways of thinking about things, and they affirmed their understanding of the lesson concepts.

Answers

Page 126

1. There are twelve possible outcomes.

H	T
H1	T1
H2	T2
H3	T3
H4	T4
H5	T5
H6	T6

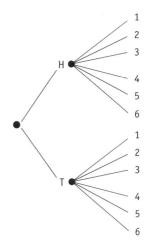

2. H2, H4, H6; 3 desired outcomes over 12 possible outcomes, $\frac{1}{4}$
3. T1, T2, T3, T4; 4 desired outcomes over 12 possible outcomes, $\frac{1}{3}$
4. H4, H6; 2 desired outcomes over 12 possible outcomes, $\frac{1}{6}$

Page 127

1. a. I   b. D   c. D   d. I
2. a. $\frac{81}{256}$; $\frac{3}{4} \times \frac{3}{4} \times \frac{3}{4} \times \frac{3}{4}$
   b. $\frac{27}{128}$; $\frac{3}{4} \times \frac{3}{4} \times \frac{3}{4} \times \frac{1}{2}$
   c. $\frac{3}{16}$; $\frac{2}{3} \times \frac{3}{4} \times \frac{3}{4} \times \frac{1}{2}$
3. a. $\frac{3}{14}$; $\frac{1}{2} \times \frac{3}{7}$
   b. $\frac{1}{14}$; $\frac{1}{2} \times \frac{3}{7} \times \frac{1}{3}$

Calculating Probability

Find the possible outcomes for each situation. Make a list of the outcomes and tell how many there are.

1 Roll a fair number cube having six sides numbered 1–6 and toss a fair penny.

Use the information from problem 1 to answer the following questions.

2 What is the probability of getting a head and an even number? Explain how you can use your list to determine this probability.

3 What is the probability of getting a tail and a number less than five? Explain how you can use your list to determine this probability.

4 What is the probability of getting a head and an even number greater than 2? Explain how you can use your list to determine this probability.

Standard 5 Data Analysis and Probability

Calculating Probability

Write the answer for each question.

1 Determine whether the events are independent or dependent. Write I or D.
   a. You toss a dime and a penny.
   b. You pick a card from a deck and do not replace it. Then you pick another card.
   c. You have two different sock drawers, one for blue socks and one for black socks. You randomly pick a drawer, then randomly pick a sock from that drawer.
   d. You have two bags. One bag contains red and green marbles, the other contains yellow and blue tiles. You pick one object from each bag.

2 You are taking a multiple-choice test with 4 questions, each of which has 4 possible answers.
   a. Suppose that you have no idea what the correct answers might be, so you take a random guess at each question. What is the probability that you will get none of the questions correct?
   b. Suppose that upon closer examination, you decide you know with absolute certainty that 2 of the choices for the last question could not possibly be correct. This leaves only 2 choices for that question. Now what is the probability that you will get none of the 4 questions correct?
   c. You take a harder look at the test and decide with absolute certainty that 1 of the choices for the first question could not be correct. What is the probability now that you will get none of the 4 questions correct?

3 You have a bag with 4 red marbles and 4 blue marbles. You randomly take 1 marble from the bag and do not put it back. Then you take a second marble from the bag.
   a. What is the probability that you have 2 red marbles?
   b. You have picked 2 marbles without replacing them and they are both red. If you remove a third marble from the bag, what is the probability that all 3 will be red?

Representing Data in Different Ways

Introduction

Objective → Students will be able to identify the means used to present data to create different perceptions.

Context → This would be one of the last lessons in graphing data. Students have had prior experiences working with data and graphs. They have both made and interpreted graphs.

NCTM Standards Focus

Students focus on how representation and communication go hand and hand. They see that there is more than one way to make a graph. They can see that a graph, like an argument, can be positioned in many different ways. By analyzing all the elements of a graph, they can learn to get as close as they can to the raw data and make their own interpretations of situations.

Representation Students look at two different graphs that represent the same set of data. They identify the differences in the graphs that make the representations look different.

Communication Students see that the main goal of a graph is communication. They understand that changes in a graph can change the message that is communicated.

Problem Solving Students see that they must really study a graph to understand what it says. They learn that all graphs are problem-solving situations where they must see for themselves what the actual information is.

Teaching Plan

Materials → Student pages 132–133; transparency of page 132 and copies for students; grid paper; graphing tools

BEGIN THE LESSON by telling students that today they are going to look at different ways to represent the same data. Tell them that they are going to hear statements from three different people who work for the same company. All the statements are correct. Read the statements one at a time and have the students discuss the meaning of each one.

One person said that the company's sales this month are double last month's sales. Ask students to evaluate the statement. Some may say that it sounds great. Others may have some reservations until they have other information.

Another person said that the company sold 5 items last month and 10 items this month. Now ask students what they think. Many will probably say that this increase is no big deal. Some, however, may hold out for more information. If students want more information, ask them what it may be. If no one asks for more information, go on to the next piece of information.

A third person said he wondered if they would sell more of the high-tech equipment if they dropped the price a little from the $2 million they are charging for each unit.

Now ask students what they think. Finally, ask them what they learned from this exercise. It is important that students understand that often information is relative and that when you look and find out the whole story you can make a more informed judgment about what is happening.

Now ask students if they can think of situations when people try to portray information in the best light for themselves. One thing that may come to mind is advertisements. Discuss this briefly, then pass out student page 132. Tell students they are looking at two graphs that present the same information. Ask them to look at both graphs and see what perception each graph gives of the information. Ask students to figure out what was done in making the graphs. Also ask them why they think someone wanted to make each graph. It may help for students to work in pairs or small groups.

HAVE THE STUDENTS DISCUSS the graph. One thing they should see is that in graph A the sales appear to be increasing more than in graph B. Students should also notice the difference in the intervals or scale on the left hand side. In graph A each interval equals ten units while in graph B the same size interval equals fifty units. Students may also notice that both graphs are broken on the vertical axis. Review what this means. However, since both of them are broken in the same way, it does not affect the comparison.

Now have students think of the different types of graphs they could make such as bar, line, pictograph, and circle. Brainstorm with them as to what influences how a graph looks.

Below are some things students might suggest. If they do not, you might want to suggest these techniques yourself. It is not important that the students learn all of these techniques.

- Changing the intervals on either axis can change how steep lines look. Ask students for an example of what would happen if the intervals for the months in graph A had been shorter (the line would have been steeper) or if the intervals for the months had been moved apart (the line would have appeared flatter).

f.y.i.

Another way to look at the axis question is to think of what makes a line steeper or flatter. It is the relationship between the intervals on each axis. For most graphs like this, there is no standard. It is up to the graph maker to determine the relationship.

- Students should understand that the interval will also affect a bar graph, but in a slightly different way. As you change the interval on the left, the bars will have the same relationship but the actual distance between the bars can change and give different visual perceptions. The changing of the horizontal axis will either widen or lengthen the bar and can change visual perceptions but probably to a lesser extent.

- If you shorten the left axis, you can distort the visual perception of a relationship. Suppose you have a bar that is 9 units high and a bar that is 10 units high. If you break the vertical axis and start it at 8 and then make the graph, the bar 10 units high will appear to be 50% taller instead of the 11% taller it would appear if you did not break the axis.

HAVE STUDENTS WORK either with a partner or in a small group to make two graphs from the same set of information. Tell them someone has been keeping track of the average high temperature for each month for a year. The information, in degrees Fahrenheit, is as follows:

January, 35; February, 39; March, 46; April, 57; May, 66; June, 74; July, 84; August, 88; September, 78; October, 66; November, 52; December, 40

Tell them to make one graph that gives the impression that the temperature does not change dramatically during the year and another that gives the impression that the temperature does change dramatically.

When students have completed their graphs, have them show each graph and discuss what they did. To make the change look less dramatic, they should have done things to flatten out the line, such as making the intervals smaller for the temperatures and/or making the space between the months wider. One other thing they could have done was to change the temperatures to degrees Celsius.

To show greater change students should have tried to make the line steeper. They could do this by making the vertical intervals wider for each degree and/or making the intervals for the months narrower.

You may wish to assign student page 133 for homework. It gives students a chance to work with a bar graph.

Student Pages

Student page 132 presents two different graphs of the same data for use during class. Student page 133 presents a situation for a bar graph.

Assessment

During the initial discussion of graphs A and B, you had an opportunity to assess students' understanding of how the graphs could show differences. As you discussed how to make graphs different you had an opportunity to judge student understandings. As students worked in groups you could make similar observations. Student page 133 gave you an opportunity to see how students understood this topic on their own.

NCTM Standards Summary

Students saw how two representations of the same information could present two different pictures of the same information. They used their reasoning and problem solving skills to see that they could use representations to communicate different perceptions. This lesson helped them understand that they need to use their mathematical tools and reasoning ability to scrutinize data that is presented to them.

Answers

Page 132
Answers may vary.

Page 133
Answers may vary.

Representing Data in Different Ways

Use the graphs to work in class.

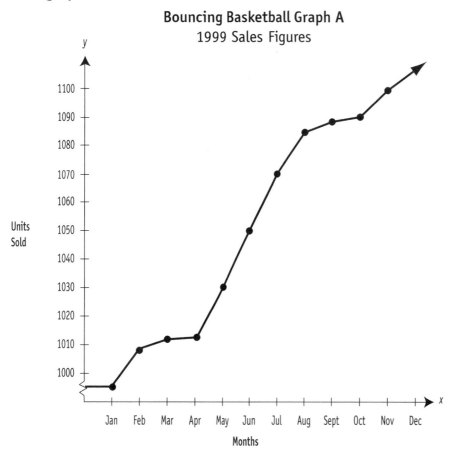

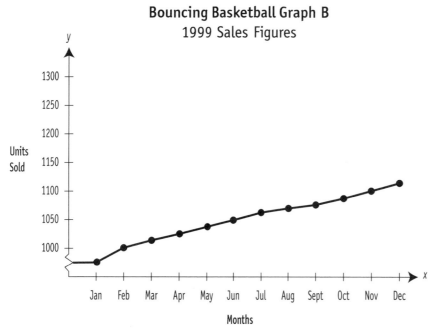

Standard 5 Data Analysis and Probability

Name _____

Representing Data in Different Ways

Use the data to make a graph.

A juice company taste-tested its new "Greatfruit Juice" against four other brands.

The results, showing the number of people who preferred each brand, are listed in the table.

Juice	Number of People
Greatfruit Juice	32
Brand A	25
Brand B	21
Brand C	14
Brand D	18

Decide whether you want to show that Greatfruit Juice is a popular juice to buy or not.

Make a graph that helps show that point of view.

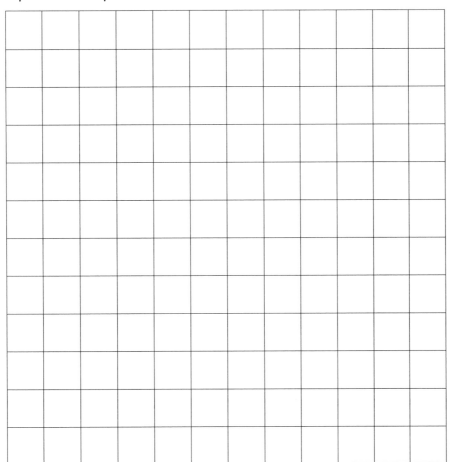

Modeling Data with Scatter Plots

Introduction

Objective → Students will make and interpret scatter plots.

Context → This lesson comes toward the end of unit on graphing linear equations or in a unit on statistics. Students have graphed linear functions and are familiar with slope and the slope-intercept form of equations. Students may go on to analyze variations in sets of data.

NCTM Standards Focus

In this standards-based lesson, students will examine real-life situations and consider how their results can be applied in a way that makes sense. Creating a scatter plot from paired data and interpreting the graphed data will help students to recognize that this form of graphic representation allows them to observe a relationship that would not be apparent from the data table. Students will create a line of best fit to summarize the relationship they observe and they will consider what conclusions are justified based on the information in the scatter plot.

Representation Students represent data sets as ordered pairs on a scatter plot and represent a line of best fit for the plot. By using these techniques, students determine if there appears to be a relationship between the two sets of data, what the relationship is, and how strong it is. Scatter plots are important tools for analyzing data, and students recognize how the line of best fit can be used to make predictions.

Communication Communication is central to helping students clarify their interpretation of the visual model. By sharing ideas, students develop strategies for drawing the lines of best fit, analyzing the relationships, and making predictions.

Connections Students use scatter plots as a tool for making connections between data sets. They consider ways in which this type of graphing can be applied in real-life situations. As they carry out the activities in this lesson, students rely on prior knowledge about lines and slope.

Teaching Plan

Materials → Student pages 138–139; graph paper

BEGIN THE LESSON by explaining that a scatter plot is a kind of graph that is used to determine if there is a relationship between two sets of data. Points on a scatter plot have an *x*-coordinate from one data set and a *y*-coordinate from another data set. The way the points are scattered shows how the data *correlate*. These ideas will become clear as students explore some scatter plots for themselves.

DISTRIBUTE STUDENT PAGE 138 and graph paper, and have students work in pairs. Tell them that the heights (in inches) and weights (in pounds) of a group of students recorded during their annual physical exams are listed in the table on the student page. Instruct students to graph the ordered pairs carefully, showing height along the *x*-axis and weight along the *y*-axis.

f.y.i.

To facilitate discussion of the scatter plot of height and weight, reproduce the completed scatter plot for display on the overhead.

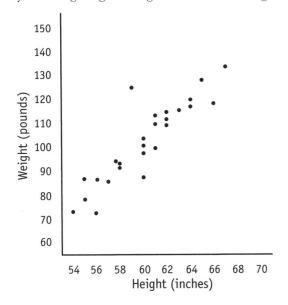

Allow about 10 minutes for students to complete their scatter plots, then begin discussion by asking students to describe the appearance of their graphs. Students should explain that most of the points are scattered near a straight line that they can visualize. Explain that when real-life data is collected, the points graphed do not usually form a straight line, but may approximate a linear relationship. When this is the case, a *line of best fit*, or a line that shows a trend, can be drawn. In this exploration, students will use their own judgment to decide where to draw the line. Have students position a straight edge in such a way that the number of points falling on either side of the straight edge seem to be fairly equal in number and there is balance in the distances of points on either side.

- *What is the relationship between height and weight that is shown in the scatter plot?* (As height increases, weight increases.)

- *Describe the slope of the line you drew.* (The slope is positive since the line slants upward from left to right.)

- *How could you use the line of best fit to predict the weight of someone who is 70 inches tall?* (Extend the line and find the weight that corresponds to an *x*-value of 70, which would be about 150 pounds.)

When one quantity increases as the other increases, the slope of the line of best fit is positive and the two sets of data are said to be *positively corre-lated.* Ask students to think of two other relationships that could be shown on a scatter plot. One is, that as one quantity increases, the other decreases. The line of best fit would slant downward from left to right. The slope of the line would be negative, and the quantities are *negatively correlated.*

The other relationship is that there may not be a relationship between the two quantities; there is no correlation. *What might the scatter plot look like?* (The points might lie in more of a circular arrangement.)

Have students spend a few minutes working together to write examples of data sets they believe would show a positive correlation, a negative correla-tion, and no correlation. Encourage them to think about the results of science experiments or business situations that they hear about in the media. This activity will reinforce their understanding of the correlation concepts while providing connections to meaningful real-life situations. Students can share their examples, and the class can decide if they agree on the relationship.

Depending on your students' preparation, you may wish to discuss how an equation for the line of best fit can be found. Review the slope-intercept form of linear relationships. Have students compute the slope using the points (57, 85) and (64, 120).

$$m = \frac{(y_2 - y_1)}{(x_2 - x_1)} \qquad m = \frac{(120 - 85)}{(64 - 57)} = \frac{35}{7} = 5$$

Substitute into the equation $y = mx + b$ to find b: $120 = 5(64) + b$; $b = {}^-200$

The equation of the line is $y = 5x - 200$.

Extension

Have students work individually or in pairs to perform an investigation or do research that yields sets of paired data. Possible relationships to research might include heights and arm lengths of classmates, area of hand and area of foot of classmates, sports performances in an Olympic event (year versus winning time), or information about the cost of a car and its repair or theft rate. Students should organize the data, make a scatter plot, determine if a relationship exists and, if so, what the relationship is. They should fit a line,

f.y.i.

Note that the graph may not convey the impression that the y-intercept is ⁻200. The distortion results from the compression of heights from 0 to 54 inches into a small space on the x-axis. Moreover, the equation points out that this linear model may make sense only for a limited range of heights and weights. For example, a 40-inch individual cannot weight 0 pounds, as predicted by the line.

use the line to make a prediction, and comment on the overall appropriateness of the model.

Student Pages

Student page 138 provides data for the lesson activity plus exercises that deal with correlation. Student page 139 presents another set of data for students to graph and interpret.

Assessment

Opportunities to assess students' understanding of scatter plots and correlation were possible as they made their height/weight graphs and interpreted them. Class discussions about relationships between data sets and use of a line of best fit, along with the exercises on the student pages, provided indicators of students' mastery of the lesson concepts and graphing techniques.

NCTM Standards Summary

Representation was the central focus of this lesson as students created a scatter plot from paired data and visualized a linear relationship. Students could recognize that this graphic representation allowed them to observe a relationship that would not have been apparent from the data table. Summarizing this relationship using a line of best fit provided students with a tool for making predictions, which is the main reason for collecting data. Discussion clarified understanding of the method of graphing and drawing the line of best fit, and communication was important as students considered conclusions that could be justified based on the scatter plot. In interpreting the graphs, students drew on prior knowledge about linear equations and slope. They also had opportunities to connect to real-life situations and consider how their results can be applied in a way that makes sense.

Answers

Page 138
1. Check students' graphs.
2. Negative
3. None
4. Positive
5. Negative
6. Positive
7. Positive
8. None

Page 139
1. Check students' graphs.
2. Positive
3. Check students' graphs.
4. Uganda; The average life expectancy seems low compared to the percent of literacy.
5. About 62, but answers will vary.

Modeling Data with Scatter Plots

Create a scatter plot.

1 Draw axis lines on a separate piece of graph paper. Label the vertical axis *Weight (pounds)* and the horizontal axis *Height (inches)* as shown in the example below. Mark weight in intervals of 10 lbs and height in intervals of 2 in. Title the graph. Plot the ordered pairs of height and weight in the table below. Be sure to graph all of the sets of height and weight.

Height (in.)	Weight (lbs)	Height (in.)	Weight (lbs)
60	97	62	114
54	72	66	117
59	94	62	109
60	102	63	115
55	78	67	132
60	100	65	127
56	72	64	120
59	96	60	86
57	90	64	116
55	86	58	93
61	109	61	99
62	111	57	85
58	91	59	124
61	113	56	86

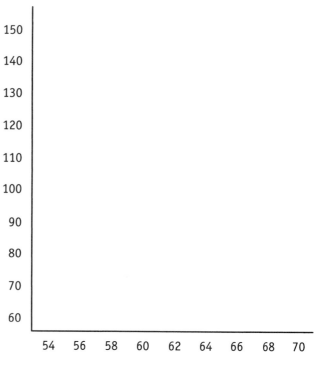

Would you expect a positive correlation, a negative correlation, or no correlation if a scatter plot were made for each of the following?

2 Weight of a car and miles per gallon

3 Price of a car and miles per gallon

4 Number of family members and average monthly use of electricity

5 Percent of a vocabulary list remembered and number of days after list was learned

6 Years of education and average annual income

7 A person's weight and blood pressure

8 Outdoor temperature and toothpaste sales

Standard 5 Data Analysis and Probability

Modeling Data with Scatter Plots

The table shows the percent of literacy and average life expectancy for 28 countries.

1 Use the data to make a scatter plot on a separate piece of graph paper. Show Percent of Literacy on the horizontal axis (suggested intervals of 5) and Average Life Expectancy on the vertical axis (suggested intervals of 10). Title the graph.

2 Does there appear to be a correlation between percent of literacy and average life expectancy? If so, what kind?

3 Draw a line of best fit.

4 Which data points seem to be exceptions to the general relationship? Explain.

5 What life expectancy would your line predict for a literacy rate of 70%?

Country	Percent of Literacy	Average Life Expectancy
Australia	100	79
Bolivia	80	60
China	82	69
Egypt	51	62
El Salvador	74	69
Ethiopia	36	47
France	99	79
Guatemala	56	65
Haiti	45	49
India	45	49
Ireland	100	76
Italy	97	78
Japan	100	80
Kenya	78	56
Liberia	38	58
Malaysia	84	70
Mexico	90	74
Nepal	28	53
New Zealand	100	77
Nicaragua	66	65
Nigeria	57	55
Peru	89	69
Portugal	87	76
Senegal	33	56
Somalia	24	55
Spain	96	79
Turkey	82	72
Uganda	62	40

Interpreting and Making Box-and-Whisker Plots

Introduction

Objective → Students will interpret and make box-and-whisker plots.

Context → Students have studied measures of central tendency and various types of graphs including stem-and-leaf plots. They will go on to work with scattergrams and to select graphs that are appropriate to the data and purpose.

Interpreting and Making Box-and-Whisker Plots

Learn

You can organize data in different ways.

Attendance at Home Basketball Games									
Stars	45	80	69	42	71	32	69	75	102
Wolves	22	99	57	65	83	24	61	82	103
Dribblers	64	111	79	88	112	48	82	99	139

A box-and-whisker plot can make it easier to make comparisons.

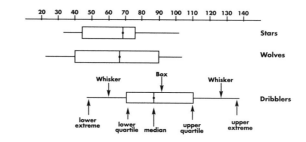

1. What is the lower quartile for each team?
2. What is the upper quartile for each team?
3. Which team had the greatest attendance? Which team had the lowest attendance?
4. What is the median for each team?

Discuss

5. Does the median help you compare the teams' attendance?
6. Which team do you think had the best attendance?

NCTM Process Standards Analysis and Focus

The standards analysis examines how the process standards have been incorporated into the above lesson. By increasing the focus on three of the process standards, a more effective and meaningful lesson can be presented. The suggestions offered can help you to think about how this might be accomplished.

Representation The student pages present data that have been translated into box-and-whisker plots as well as data to be used by students to create plots.

Suggestion → Increase the amount of time allotted to examining the components of box-and-whisker plots to emphasize what information is represented and how. Present students with a step-by-step method for creating the

Practice

Find the median, the upper extreme, the lower extreme, the upper quartile, and the lower quartile for each set of data.

1.

Attendance at School Plays				
167	117	100	154	119
143	161	159	144	190
93	122	134	110	104

2.

Basketball Game Scores				
54	47	68	66	74
39	43	86	64	47
56	88	73	101	91

3.

Science Test Scores				
75	78	67	79	89
93	77	85	82	80
63	96	82	86	73

Mr. Lopez is supervising raffle ticket sales by students in Grades 6, 7, and 8. Use the Average Daily Sales to answer questions 4 through 8 below.

Average Daily Sales								
Grade 6	112	119	132	166	187	154	140	140
Grade 7	99	104	102	120	132	144	124	120
Grade 8	144	133	120	127	144	188	192	199

4. Which class had the widest range of sales?

5. Which class had the widest range between upper and lower quartiles?

6. Which class had the highest upper quartile sales?

7. Which class has the highest median sales average?

8. Is the lower extreme a good indicator of which class had the lowest overall sales performance?

plots. This will aid them in interpreting these types of graphs.

Reasoning and Proof Most questions on the student pages call for students to interpret data, but they require minimal reasoning. The lesson poses a few questions that the teacher notes say encourage discussion, but no guidance is provided for what should be included in the discussion.

Suggestion → Encourage students to interpret the overall picture presented by the graph and the information that can be gained from it instead of concentrating only on specifics. Have students consider reasons for making such a graph and why it is useful. In this way, students will gain insight into functions that these graphs can serve, and they will be able to recognize the unique advantages of box-and-whisker plots over other displays.

Communication Communication in the lesson consists mainly of answering direct questions about the box-and-whisker plots shown and the tabular data students will use to create plots. Questions can be completed as a written exercise; discussion is not involved.

Suggestion → An increased focus on why and how box-and-whisker plots are created and the information they convey will open up communication. Initiate discussion that helps students interpret as well as construct this type of graph. This will help students gain insight into the advantages and disadvantages offered by box-and-whisker plots and how they can be used along with other methods of data analysis.

Problem Solving Interpreting graphs requires reasoning but does not involve problem solving.

Connections The teacher notes suggest using information from a stem-and-leaf plot to make a box-and-whisker plot. Connections to dealing with measures of central tendency are imbedded in the activities.

The teaching plan that follows shows how the suggestions for increasing the focus on the process standards can be implemented.

Revised Teaching Plan

f.y.i.

In box-and-whisker plots, the whiskers are the lines at the left and right of the box. These graphs are commonly referred to more simply as box plots, and that term will be used in this lesson.

BEGIN THE LESSON by explaining that even when data are organized in a table, they may be difficult to analyze, especially if we are interested in how much variation there is in the data. The range gives some information about how the data are spread out, but since it is computed using extreme values, the range does not tell much about the other values in the set. A box plot is a visual representation of how the data are spread out and how much variation there is.

Using the tables and graphs presented here will facilitate discussion. If you prefer, use the data in your text and adapt the questions accordingly.

Average Monthly Temperatures

	Jan	Feb	Mar	Apr	May	June	July	Aug	Sept	Oct	Nov	Dec
San Diego, CA	57	59	60	62	64	67	71	73	71	68	62	57
Dallas, TX	43	48	57	66	73	81	85	85	77	67	56	47
Charleston, SC	48	51	58	65	73	78	82	81	76	67	58	51

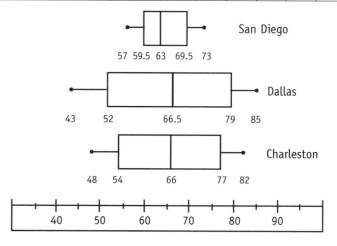

Explain that in each box plot, 50% of the values are above the middle or median of the data and 50% are below it. The median is represented by the mark found inside the box. The first quartile, which represents the median of the lower 50% of the values, is the left side of the box. The third quartile, which represents the median of the upper 50% of the values, is the right side of the box. The values represented by each of these indicators can be determined by using the scale below the plots.

DRAW ATTENTION TO THE TABLE to have students determine what comparisons can be made easily about the climates of the three cities from this representation. *What comparisons about the climates of the three cities can be made easily from the table?* (Highs and lows, range of temperatures) *Which city appears to have the most variable climate? The least variable climate? Explain your answers. Can you tell which city has the highest median temperature?* Involving students in this type of discussion will help them to recognize the need for a method of representation that allows us to see these important characteristics of the data at a glance.

Emphasize that the purpose of a box plot is to represent a set of data to show certain key values and how the data are spread out. Examples of how these plots are used include aiding schools to get an overall picture of how groups of students performed in testing, and analyzing items in a production line to see how they are meeting quality standards.

Next, present the steps for making a box plot. Use the temperature graphs to illustrate each of the components.

- First, arrange the data in increasing order. Identify the lowest value, the median, and the highest value. Also find the lower quartile (the median of the lower half of the data) and the upper quartile (the median of the upper half of the data).
- Next, plot the five values found in step 1 on a number line. Above it, draw a rectangular box, the length of which extends from the lower quartile to the upper quartile, indicating the median with a vertical line extending through the box.
- Finally, connect the lowest value to the lower quartile with a line (one "whisker") and the upper quartile to the highest value with another line (the other "whisker".)

Have students examine the temperature plots. *What is San Diego's median temperature?* (63°) *Which city has the highest median temperature?* (Dallas) *Which city experiences the greatest temperature range?* (Dallas) *What percent of the data does each whisker represent?* (25%) *Each part of the box?* (25%) *The whole box?* (50%) *How many temperatures does each whisker represent?* (3; there are 12 data entries divided equally among the four

f.y.i.

If there are an odd number of data values, the overall median is not included among the values used to find the medians of either the lower or upper quartiles.

Example: 24, 26, 30, 35, 37, 43, 50

Lower extreme 24
  median of 1st quartile 26.6
Upper extreme 50
  median of 3rd quartile 43.36
Overall median 35

quartiles.) By answering these questions, students will make the connections between the data and the components of the graph.

Involve students in a discussion of the visual impressions created by the three temperature plots. *Which city seems to have the greatest range in its climate? Why?* (Dallas; its graph is the most spread out.) *San Diego's graph has a short box and short whiskers; what does this mean?* (If a whisker or a box is short, this means the data are concentrated over a narrow range of values.) These questions will help students understand how to interpret the information represented.

Focus students' attention on the original table of data and the graphs. *What are some advantages and disadvantages of representing the data in the table?* (Advantage: all individual data are shown; disadvantage: it's difficult to see how data are distributed.) *What are some advantages and disadvantages of representing data in a box plot?* (Advantage: easy to see range, median, and so on; gives visual impression of spread; disadvantage: individual data are lost.)

HELP STUDENTS DEVELOP THEIR SKILLS in making and interpreting box plots. Pair students and have them create box plots that represent the sets of math quiz scores shown for students in two classes. Instruct your students to use their completed graphs to answer the questions listed.

> **Class A:** 70, 73, 67, 80, 85, 98, 81, 68, 72, 75
> **Class B:** 59, 80, 89, 86, 78, 72, 75, 84, 87, 94

1. Which class has the greater range for the top 25% of the scores? (Class A)

2. Which class has the greater range for the middle 50% of the scores? (Class B)

3. Describe the distribution of the scores in the two classes. (Class A's scores range from 67 to 98, with the middle 50% of scores between 70 and 81; Class B's scores range from 59 to 94, with the middle 50% of scores between 75 and 87.)

4. Which class seems to have done better? Give reasons for your answer. (Class A has a higher top score, and Class B has a lower low score, but the quartiles and median for Class B are 75, 82, and 87, whereas for Class A the numbers are 70, 74, and 81. Therefore, the middle range for Class B is much higher.)

CLOSE THE LESSON by challenging students to explain the conditions under which a set of data would have a box plot like the one shown on this page. Students should explain that this plot would occur when the greatest value and the upper quartile were the same number.

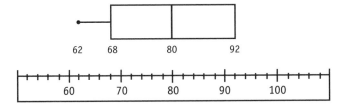

Extension

Have students create another pair of box plots or study a pair of box plots that look similar but that contain completely different data. For example, a plot for the data 1, 1, 2, 5, 7, 8, 8 and the other for 1, 4, 4, 5, 6, 6, 6. Discuss the implications; looking at these graphs can be deceptive because the individual values are not represented.

Student Pages

Students are now ready to complete exercises similar to those on the reduced student pages.

Assessment

As students responded to questions, you could assess their skills at finding specific information and interpreting the overall impression of this type of graph. There were opportunities to observe students constructing graphs and to evaluate their understanding of the steps involved in the process.

NCTM Standards Summary

Close examination of the components of box plots helped students to understand how their graphical representation was related to original data. Questions engaged students' reasoning powers and encouraged them to interpret the overall picture as well as the specific data represented. Considering the purposes these graphs serve made the graphs more meaningful and justified their importance. In-depth discussions helped students identify the information contained in the box plots and reinforced the steps used to construct them. By comparing various forms of representing data, students were able to recognize how information can be learned more easily from these graphs then from using summary statistics.

Create Your Own Lesson

THIS LAST CHAPTER IS DESIGNED TO HELP you develop your own lessons in which you can comfortably incorporate the NCTM standards with your teaching style. We start with a list of questions to help you focus on factors to consider as you begin to organize a standards-based lesson. Then, we model the process used to create a lesson as you are walked through the thoughts and decisions one person used in developing a lesson.

The questions listed here are meant as a guide, a starting point; they are offered to get you thinking about how to develop your lesson, what material to cover, what steps to follow, what questions to ask. Hopefully, these questions will trigger additional ideas that you will add as you go along.

Write down the ideas that come to you as you read each question. There may be questions for which you don't have an immediate response, but don't worry; as you begin working on your lesson, ideas will come. Start by selecting the general content area. Think about the concept you want to develop. Then, narrow in on an objective for the lesson. Be specific and be realistic. What does meeting that objective mean? Is there a skill that students should be able to perform after completing the lesson? Are there questions they should be able to answer? How will you determine that the objective has been met?

Next, think about the process standards: Problem Solving, Reasoning and Proof, Communication, Connections, and Representation. What approach will be effective in helping students understand the concept? Try to envision how the lesson will flow, how it should begin, what activities and questions will be included, and how you will assess learning. Understand that there can be several ways to successfully teach any lesson. As you begin to design your lesson, new ideas will come and you will be able to refine your thinking.

Focusing Questions

1. What content standard is to be addressed? What concept within that standard is to be developed?

2. What information do the standards offer about this content?

3. What do students know about this content? What don't they know?

4. What is the specific objective of the lesson? What should students be able to do at the end of the lesson?

recognize	identify	define
review	compute	classify
compare	create	other

5. What kinds of questions should students be able to answer when they complete this lesson? What skill(s) should they be able to demonstrate?

6. What resources are available to develop this concept?

references	textual material
manipulatives	supplementary material
colleagues	student knowledge

7. What can realistically be accomplished in the time allowed?

8. Which activities and process standards can best help develop the key ideas?
   - using drawings, charts, diagrams (Representation)
   - focusing on symbols (Representation)
   - conducting small-group/large-group discussion (Communication)
   - having students gather and analyze data (Problem Solving)
   - thinking through relationships and explaining them (Reasoning and Proof and Communication)
   - finding ways to prove thinking and verify solutions (Reasoning and Proof)
   - extending/building on former knowledge (Connections)
   - integrating the concept with another discipline (Connections)
   - relating math to its use in the real world (Connections)

9. What questions will focus students' thinking on the concept and help guide learning?

Developing the Lesson

I'M DEVELOPING A LESSON that will have students solve percentage problems. I also want students to look for patterns and relationships in numbers rather than simply compute percentages. I know that my students are generally proficient at solving percentage problems. But I sometimes think that they're just reading the problems and deciding which numbers need to be manipulated; the thinking seems rote and mechanized. I want them to think on a higher mathematical level, to consider patterns occurring within a collection of data. I don't think my students use percentages very much in their daily lives. I know they're constantly exposed to lots of information presented in percentage form, like statistics and surveys on the news, but seeing percentages is certainly different from using them. I want these students to work with some percentages in a realistic way.

I have two objectives for this lesson. The first is to have students successfully find the relationships among numbers in a real-world data set. The second is to have students use these numbers to solve some rich percentage problems. A problem-solving approach will do this.

Since mathematical reasoning and proof is so important, I'm going to have students look for patterns or relationships among numbers. Students need to be able to explain their procedures and justify their answers. Communication will be stressed in this lesson, as I expect the students to state patterns or relationships between numbers, and to present solutions to some large real-world-based problems.

As I continue to formulate this lesson in my head, I'm realizing the students will need many numbers with which to work. If they are to see patterns or relationships and use the data to problem solve, I think they'll have to logically represent or organize the information, perhaps by making accurate tables or charts, or even using a computer spreadsheet program. I also know that not everyone will see the same patterns or relationships, so representing the data will help students use words or symbols to communicate what they observe.

I know I want the class to work with a realistic situation, so connections should be evident. I also know that working with percentages will automatically have the class involved in other areas of math, like decimals and fractions. The lesson is taking shape.

I need to be clear on exactly what the students will do in this lesson. Well, I know I want the students to have some data to analyze, so I'll need to come up with some. I also know I want them to use that information later in problems. I think if I can come up with a good real-world context for the problem, all the details will fall into place.

As I look for real-world situations I don't think I want to use any consumer or shopping settings; I think the students have already worked a lot in the past with sales taxes and discounts. I'd like to come up with something a little more interesting, something where the calculations really matter. I have been to some workshops where we have had to make group decisions—like what to take on a trip out of the woods if the group were lost. This type of situation, where people have to decide what to carry, could work with a regular backpacking trip. I can work with the concept of what percentage of a person's body weight he or she could carry.

Problems in real life sometimes require numerical answers. But more often, people use mathematical information to make "yes/no" decisions. I'd like my problem to work in this second way, which I think is more realistic. I also like this kind of problem because it can be more open-ended, allowing students to solve it in multiple ways.

I'll provide the students with the information on the people and the gear. They will need to look for patterns and relationships. The numbers in this chart were carefully calculated so that each person would be close to carrying 35% of his or her weight, since most backpacking guides suggest a hiker carry no more than 35–40% of his or her weight. I will make sure there is a little extra room for them to take on more weight, if needed. I worked the lesson using the numbers and made adjustments to make sure students confronted the situations I wanted them to.

	A	B	C	D	E
Mary	140	32	18	50	35.71%
Claire	150	37	19	56	37.33%
Steve	175	45	19	64	36.57%
Patrick	210	53	19	72	34.28%

This same data will be used for the percentage problems. I will intentionally not label the columns so the students can try to figure out the relationships among the numbers. However, I do want students to try to determine what

Group Gear List
All weights are in pounds
tent A: 8
tent B: 6
water purifier: 2
pots/pans: 3
stove: 1
fuel: 4 cans @2 each: 8
rope: 7
first aid kit: 2
maps: 1
GPS: 2
tarp: 1
spices: 1
saw: 1
hatchet: 1
utensils: 1
supertool: 1
pasta:2
trail mix: 4
oatmeal: 4
noodles: 3
instant potatoes: 1
coffee: 1
freeze-dried meals: 4
energy bars: 8
binoculars: 1
blanket: 1

the columns are. I want students to see how the numbers within a column are related. I also want them to notice relationships among the columns and the rows. The second problem will require more numerical data for problem solving: a list of the gear the group is taking on the backpacking trip and how much each item weighs. I chose items that are commonly used on backpacking trips, but placed the weights in pounds rather than ounces so the students wouldn't get bogged down in the computation. I also included a lot of one or two pound items, so there could be many ways of solving the problems.

Problem 1

Work in groups. Study the chart. What patterns or relationships among numbers do you see? What relationships among the columns do you see? What do you think the column headings could be? Represent the patterns or relationships using words, sentences, or symbols.

Discussing Problem 1

What patterns or relationships do you see? The students should discover that column D is the sum of columns B and C. I expect most of the class to see this. Column B refers to the amount of personal gear each hiker has in their backpack.

In what ways were you able to represent this? I expect students to use words ("B plus C equals D"), sentences ("When you add B and C together you get D"), and formulas ($D = B + C$). I'll emphasize that representations are important because they articulate the patterns or relationships that exist in a situation. *In what other ways could you represent the relationship among B, C, and D?* I'll ask this to help them see a wide variety of methods of representing and communicating mathematical patterns and relationships. *What do you think each column represents?* Students with backpacking or camping experience might have a better sense of this than others, but I think most of the students should be able to figure some of these out: A is the hiker's body weight, B is the weight in personal gear the hiker is carrying, C is the weight in group gear the hiker is carrying, D is the total amount of weight the hiker has in the backpack, and E is the percentage of body weight the hiker is carrying. I will record this on an overhead of the chart. Also, I will probably help student groups with this information during their working session using questions while they are working.

I expect that another relationship–$E = D/A$–could be more difficult for the students to figure out. *Is there anything about the numbers in column E that give you a clue?* I'll ask this to help the students see that numbers can yield clues about their relationship to other numbers; in this case the numbers contain decimals, meaning they are the result of some calculation. *What operations with whole numbers often yield answers with decimals?* This offers the class another clue. When students present conjectures I will ask them to support them with clear examples, and also allow the class members to challenge them further. *Does the fact that the column E numbers are in percentages reveal anything about their relationship to the other columns?* I'll ask this for two reasons: to help the class see the relationship between E, A, and D; and to mention that, if students are looking for patterns or relationships, they need to be aware of clues within the data. In this case, the percentages are a helpful bit of information to be used in detecting relationships within this problem.

Problem 2

The backpackers have decided that it's not fair for each hiker to carry the same amount of group supplies, because the hikers are not all the same size and won't eat the same amount of food. Instead, they decide to distribute the group gear by each hiker's percentage of the overall group body weight. Determine each hiker's percentage of the group body weight, then distribute the group gear so that each hiker is carrying the correct percentage.

Discussing Problem 2

For this problem, I will use the information from problem 1, but with labels for the columns. Students will be encouraged to make charts and tables for this problem to show their thinking and solutions. *How did you determine each hiker's percentage of the group's body weight?* I'll ask this to see how they solved the problem and worked with percentages. I think the students will be able to use the formula for "percent of body weight carried" to help figure this out: divide the hiker's individual weight by the combined weight of all the hikers. If the hiker represents 28% of the group rate, he or she must carry 28% of the group gear.

Students should arrive at these values: Mary must carry 21% of the weight, Claire 22%, Steve 26%, and Patrick 31%. *How much weight in group-gear is each hiker carrying? How did you calculate the percentage?* I'll help students clarify areas in which they're confused. At this point students will present their answers to the problem. There are a variety of solutions, but each hiker should carry the following amount of group gear: Mary–15.75 lb., Claire–16.5 lb., Steve–19.5lb., and Patrick–about 23.25 lb.

When students present their solutions it should be a good time for the class to check everyone else's accuracy and reasoning. *What will you do about half-pounds and quarter pounds? Should you round? Estimate?* I'll ask this to generate a short discussion, because I think there will be a variety of opinions on what to do with the decimals. It may lead to a discussion of how to solve the problem in real life versus how to solve it on paper. This is a nice distinction to draw. Communicating solutions, decisions, and methods, and defending them, should help all of the students hone their mathematical thinking.

Problem 3

Steve begins to falter because of the amount of weight carried in his backpack. He can only carry 55 lbs. Redistribute some of his weight to the other hikers in a way that you think will make it possible for the hikers to finish the trip. Determine the percentage of body weight each person should carry.

Discussing Problem 3

I'll ask volunteers to give their solutions and their methods of arriving at them. *How did you redistribute Steve's extra weight?* I'll ask this because the solutions will vary depending on what the students initially had Steve carry. But regardless, he must be carrying 9 or so fewer pounds, and those pounds must be shifted to the other hikers. Student responses can be debated and analyzed. *What percentage of body weight is each hiker now carrying?*

Again, answers will depend on what items are redistributed from Steve's pack, and to whom. *Why did you redistribute in that way?* I ask this to hear students reasoning, to see what thinking went into who received what. Was the gear equally distributed to the other three hikers, or did the student look at the weights each was already carrying and decide who was in the best position to take on more weight? The answer to this question can reveal whether the student thought through the ramifications of putting more weight on other hikers. It might be easy for a student to simply transfer the weight onto Mary, reasoning that "She's carrying the least so she can take on more." As far as real problem solving goes, this approach solves one problem only to create another. This is something I'd like to bring into the discussion—even though there are many ways to solve this problem, some ways are better than others.

Reviewing the Plan

I believe that the pattern/relationship problem at the start of the lesson will make the students more able to solve the backpacking problems. I think the lesson as a whole can be a success because of the process standards and their focus on helping the students think. The problem-solving nature of the lesson, along with students reasoning, representing, communicating, and connecting mathematical ideas, should, I think, enrich their conceptual understandings. I believe that after taking part in the lesson, the students should be able to more successfully notice mathematical patterns and improve their ability to work with percentages.